THE GREAT BOOK OF
BRAINTEASERS

PUZZLES COMPILED BY NORMAN SULLIVAN
with contributions from Ken Russell & Philip Carter

Published by Igloo Books Limited
Henson Way
Kettering
Northants
NN16 8PX
info@igloo-books.com

This edition published 2004

Typeset by MATS, Southend-on-Sea, Essex

Copyright © Lyness Publications, 2004

ISBN 1-84193-260-4

Printed in China

Contents

Introduction

The Great Book of Brainteasers is packed full of visual, word and number puzzles designed to entertain and test you at the same time.

There are over 400 puzzles which will challenge you and help develop your IQ, although do remember that they are not IQ tests! The puzzles vary in difficulty and are not arranged in any particular order, but be assured that there is a good mix throughout the book.

You will see that some puzzles have a page to themselves and are illustrated with pictures or diagrams. They are a little different to the rest of the book and are designed to give you a bit of breathing space before diving back into the puzzles.

The answers are at the back of the book, but we recommend that you only check them if you really need to. It really is much more fun to try and work the puzzles out for yourself!

Puzzles

1 Which is the odd one out?

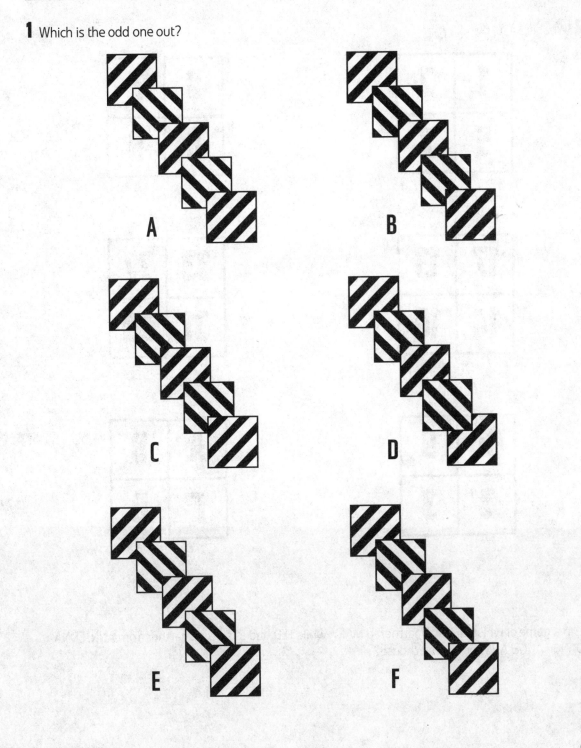

2 What are A, B, C and D?

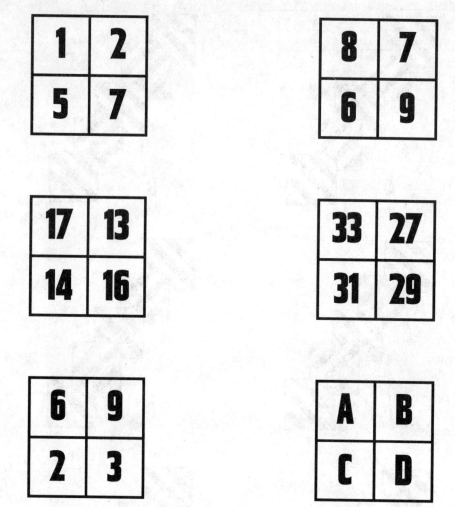

3 In a game of whist, GEORGE partnered MARY, while TED had to select a partner from ANN, EDNA, JOAN or ANGELA. Whom did he choose?

4 Which door is wrong?

A

B

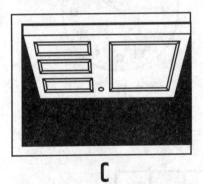

C

D

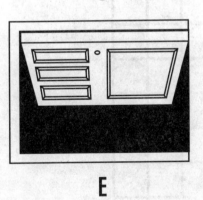

E

F

5 Which clock is the odd one out?

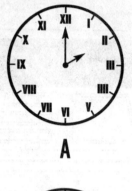

A

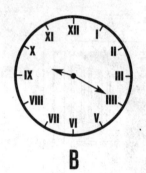

B

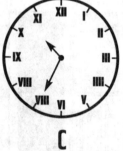

C

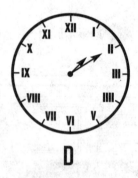

D

6 How many squares are there here?

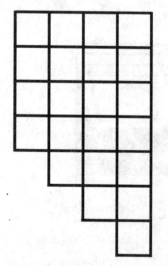

7 Which is the odd one out?

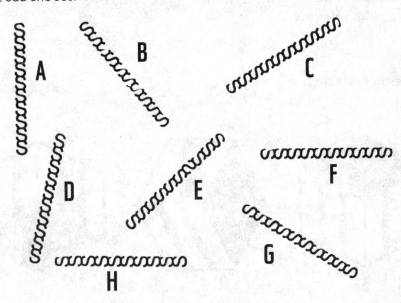

8 Counting down, first by one place, then by two places, then by three and so on (adding one extra place each time), as in this example – 15, 14, 12, 9, 5, 0 – which of these numbers will finish at zero?

102 103 104 105 106

9 How many triangles are there here?

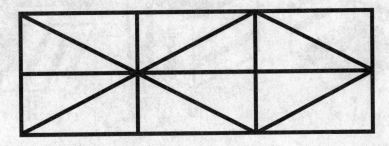

10 In a party of 35 people there are twice as many women as children and twice as many children as men. How many of each are there?

11 Arrange these cubes into four matching pairs

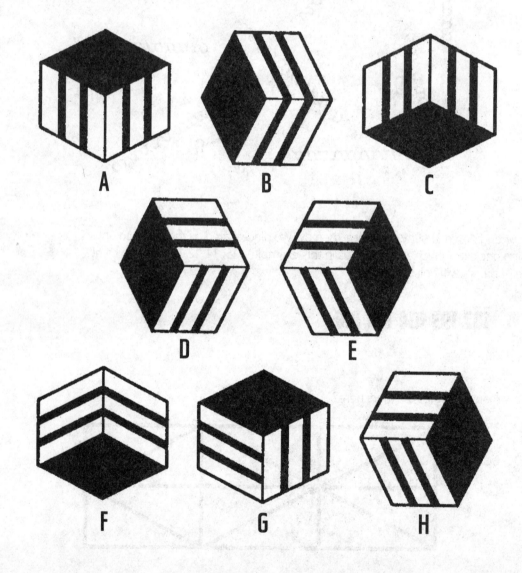

HORSE-RACE

12 There was a 16 horse race in progress at the race-course, but I missed the finish. I asked 6 of my friends to tell me the number of the winner. These were their answers.

A It was even

B It was odd

C It was prime

D It was a square number

E It had 2 digits

F It was between 6 and 12

But only four had told the truth. Which number was the winner?

Puzzle 13

SOCKS

13 A blind man had only black or white socks.
In his drawer he had 4 socks. He went to the drawer and took out 2 socks.

The chances that he had a pair of white socks was $\frac{1}{2}$.

What were the chances that he had drawn out a pair of black socks?

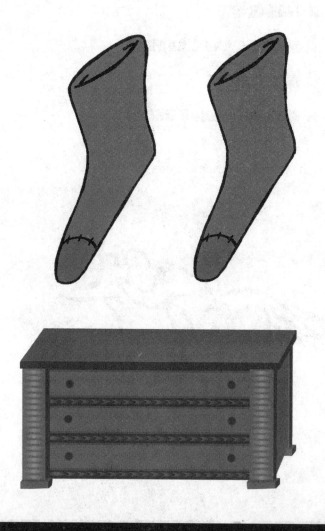

14 Choosing from the numbers below, what are A, B, C and D?

$$(A \times B + C) - D = 5$$

6 6 9 12

15 Which of the following statements are true and which are false?

A. If this clock is gaining, the pendulum weight should be moved downwards.

B. The majority of these shapes are convex.

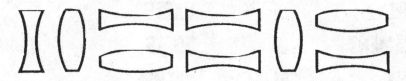

C. A spider has six legs

D. The majority of these are stalagmites.

Puzzle 16

GROUPS

16 These twelve names of groups of creatures have been mixed up. Can you re-arrange them?

SIEGE	of	HERMITS
TRIP	of	HARPERS
HUSK	of	LARKS
EXALTATION	of	CRANES
MELODY	of	NIGHTINGALES
OBSERVANCE	of	OWLS
WATCH	of	RABBITS
TRIBE	of	SHEEP
KENNEL	of	HARES
PARLIAMENT	of	GOATS
COLONY	of	RACHES
CRY	of	HOUNDS

17 From the example given below, decide what goes into the empty bracket below.

5 1 2 (4 2 3 5 1 6) 6 4 3

7 8 6 (   ) 4 1 2

18 If

13 x 3 = 40

12 x 3 = 35

15 x 3 = 46

and **16 x 3 = 47**

what does **17 x 3 = ?**

19 How many hexagons (six-sided figures) can you find here?

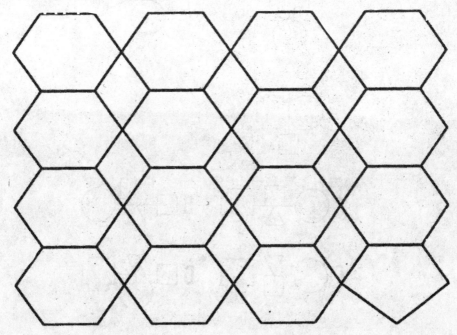

20 Which of the figures at the bottom A, B or C, should take the place of number 3?

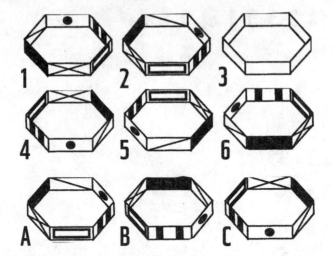

21

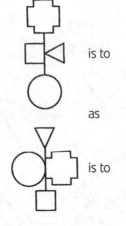

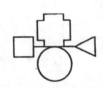

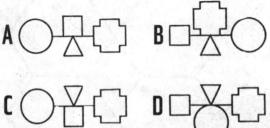

WATER BUTT

22 Two farm labourers were arguing about a water butt. One said it was less than half full and the other said it was more than half full.
To settle the argument they asked the farmer to adjudicate.

Although there were no other implements or vessels at hand with which to measure the water, the farmer was quickly able to determine who was correct. How did he do it?

23 What number goes into the empty brackets?

16 (4 2 5 6)

9 (3 8 1)

25 (   )

24 Which is the odd one out?

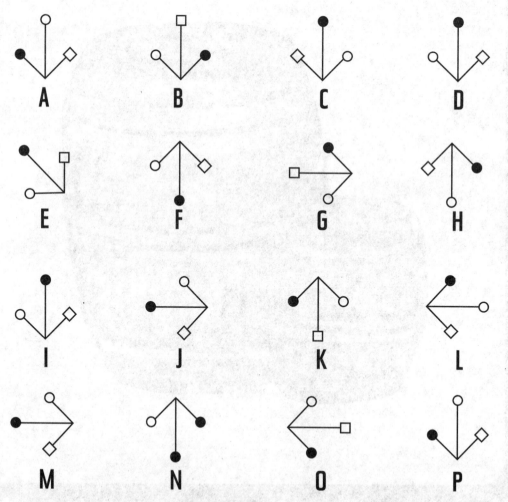

25 If I had one more sister I would have twice as many sisters as brothers. If I had one more brother I would have the same number of each. How many brothers and sisters have I?

26 Using your eyes only and without the aid of a pointer, trace which of the numbered lines will reach any of the goals marked A, B and C. State the number of the line and the goal reached. Right angles must be used only when there is no alternative route.

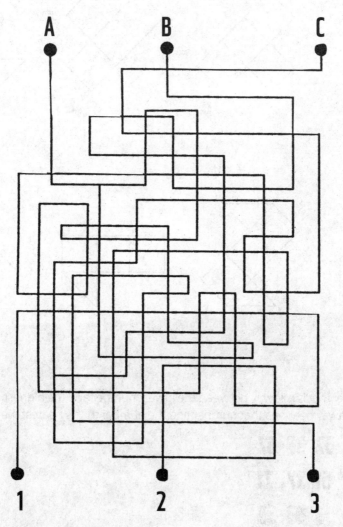

27 A bag contains 64 balls of eight different colours. There are eight of each colour (including red). What is the least number you would have to pick, without looking, to be sure of selecting 3 red balls?

28 Arrange these shapes into four pairs

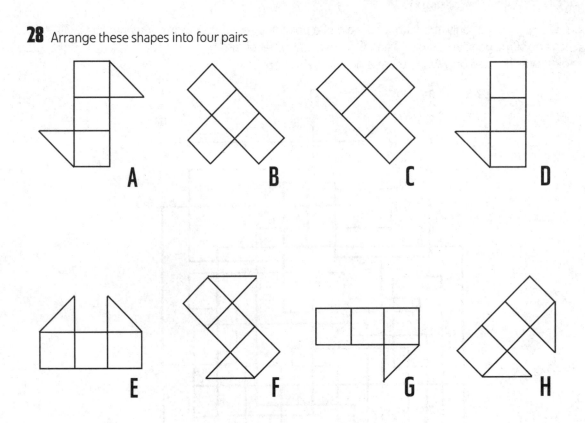

A B C D

E F G H

29 Select the number that is midway between the lowest number and the highest number. Which number is midway between that number and the number that is nearest the highest number?

35　5　52　36　67

69　4　51　37　71

55　68　3　53　39

30 Which is the smallest segment and which is the largest segment in this circle?

31 Eleven posts have been erected in a straight line and on level ground at regular intervals. Ten are of equal length. Which one is a different length?

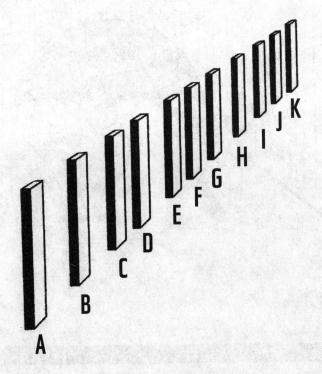

Puzzle 32

GOLF

32 Two men A and B played a round of golf. A said to B, let us play for a wager on each hole, we will play for half of the money in my wallet at each hole. I have £100 in my wallet, so for the first hole we will play for a stake of £50. If I win you will give me £50, and if I lose you will be given £50. On the second hole I will either have £150 in my wallet or £50, so we will play for £75 or £25.

After the 12th hole it started to rain, so they stopped the game and went back to the club house. As A had won 6 holes and B only 4 holes with 2 holes being tied, A said I will buy the drinks. To his amazement, he had only £71.18 in his wallet.

Why was this possible? It makes no difference in the order of winning the holes.

COLLEGE

33 At college, 70% of the students studied Maths, 75% studied English, 85% studied French and 80% studied German.

What percentage at least must have studied all 4?

34 From the numbers below and using each number only once in each set, select at least five sets of three that add to 29:

18 6 13 9 19 12

11 4 10 5 8 17

35 Which spanner fits the nut?

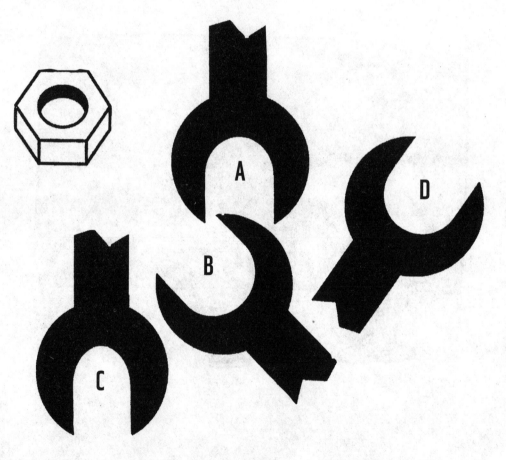

36 A sheet of paper is folded in half and cuts made into it. The paper is then unfolded to reveal this shape. Which of the figures – A, B, C or D – shows the original cuts?

37 How many diamonds are there here?

JAPAN

38 This sign was seen in Japan. What does it mean?

PHU2LUL9

HOUR GLASS

39 With a 7 minute hour glass and an 11 minute hour glass, what is the quickest way to time the boiling of an egg for 15 mins?

40 If a pack of playing cards measures 1.3cm when viewed sideways, what would be the measurement if all the aces were removed?

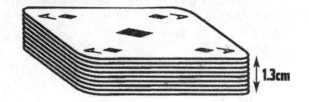

41 Match these designs into six pairs.

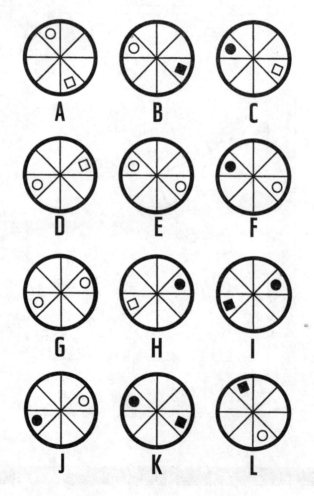

42 Which is the second smallest circle and which is the second largest circle?

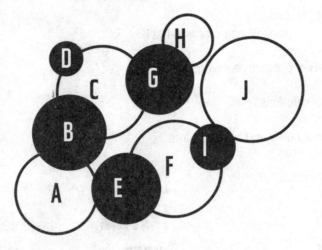

43 Which two dominoes are missing from the set?

PAIR WORDS

44 Here are two lists of words.
List A, each word has two possible pair words in List B.

List B, each word has two possible pair words in List A.

There are two possible solutions.

Pair a word from each list until you have 10 pairs.

List A	List B
SEVERN	TRACTOR
ARROW	RIVER
TURRET	BULLS–EYE
FARM	BOW
YARBOROUGH	TANK
SAND	CARDS
YEW	CASTLE
VEHICLE	BANK
RIPARIAN	WOOD
JACK	BRIDGE

45 Consider the following and decide which is the odd one out.

A. 6 + 17 - 9 ÷ 7 + 3

B. 3 x 11 + 6 ÷ 13 + 2

C. 2 x 6 x 3 + 4 ÷ 10

D. 1 + 8 - 3 ÷ 2 + 2

E. 7 - 4 + 6 - 1 - 3

46 Which of these designs match each other?

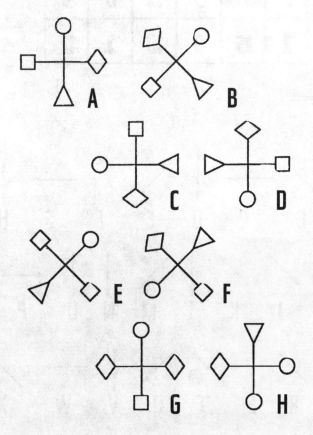

47 What is the total of the four blank squares in the centre when appropriate numbers are filled in?

1	2	9	1	2	3
8	3	3	4	7	5
4	5			5	6
5	9			4	11
7	8	3	13	8	9
2	15	9	10	1	17

48 Which is the odd one out

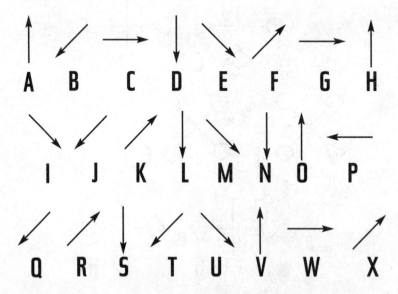

49 What should go into the last line in the left-hand column?

1812	**9234**
2421	**6437**
1556	**3578**
1436	**2794**
- - - -	**2545**

50 Which of these contains the greatest number of triangles?

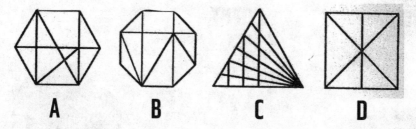

A   **B**   **C**   **D**

51

is to

as

is to

Choose from A, B or C

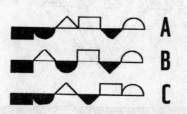

A

B

C

WHAT'S IN A NAME?

52 Arrange the following female names and male names into groups of three:

OLIVE   ISABEL

PRIMROSE   MYRTLE

GARNET   DIAMOND

PEARL   SANDY

MARTIN   MAVIS

ROBIN   POPPY

53 If 1 = X, 2 = C and 3 = M, what is $\frac{3}{2} + \frac{2}{1}$?

54 If the two spirals at the top are correct, which, if any, of those below are wrong?

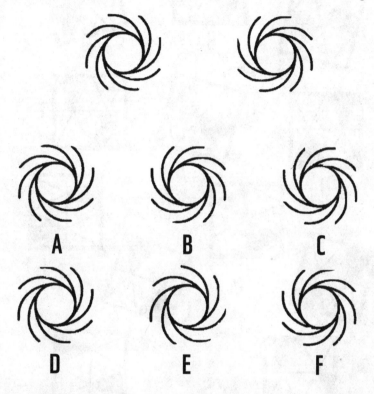

A   B   C

D   E   F

55 What goes into the empty brackets?

3 4 5 6 (7 1)

6 5 9 2 (1 1 7)

7 2 5 1 (9 4)

9 5 9 2 (   )

56 Match these patterns into four groups of three and state which is the odd one out.

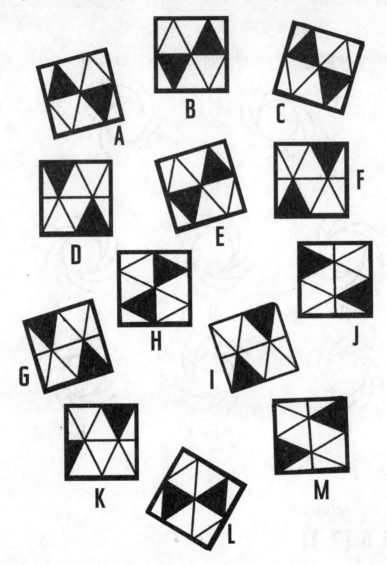

57 What comes next?

1 4 21 13 2 18 1 20 –

58 Which of these matchstick men is the odd man out?

59 The shape of wallpaper at the top has already been hung.
Which two of the sheets below will exactly match it when pasted on each side of it?

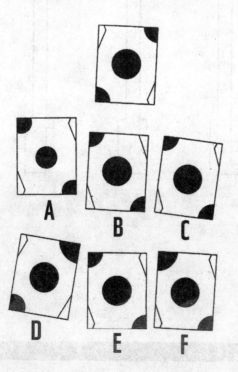

Puzzle 60

KEY SEQUENCE

60 The safe can only be opened by using the keys in the correct order that spells out a word. What is that word? Every key must be used just once.

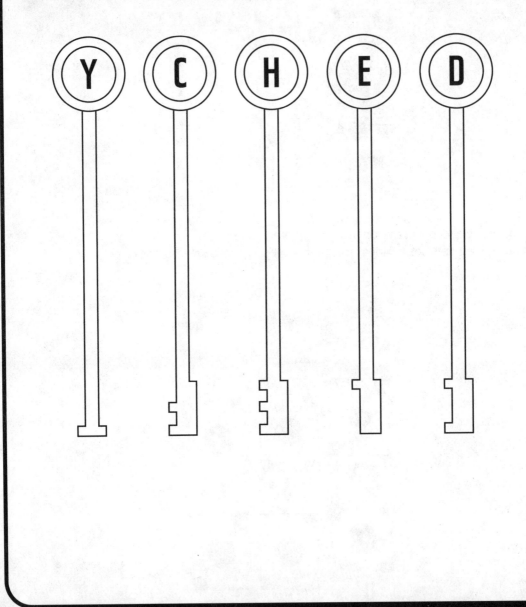

61 If the top clocks are right, which of those below are wrong?

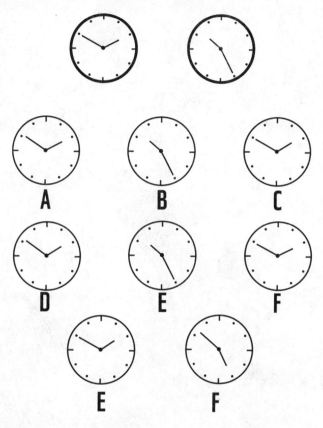

62 Which is the odd one out?

63 Which is the odd one out?

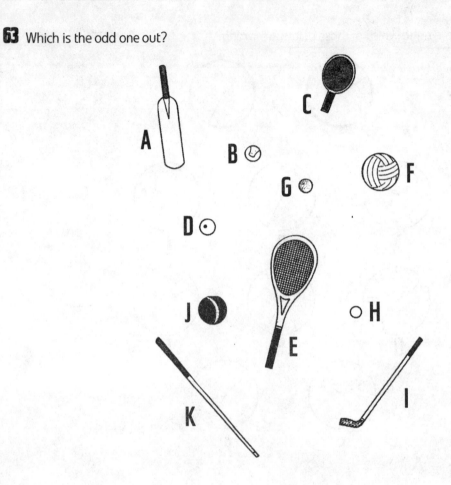

64 Which one spoils the pattern?

1 2 3 4 5 6 7 8 9 10 11 12 13 14 15 16 17 18 19 20 21

A Losing Streak

65 At the casino I had to pay a £1 entrance fee. I also gave the cloakroom girl £1 tip each evening. Each day for four days I lost half of the money I had left. I went home with £1. How much did I have to start with?

Puzzle 66

CENSUS

66 A census taker called at a man's house and said, "what are the ages of your 3 daughters?"

The man said "If you multiply their ages together it equals 72 and if you add them it equals your door number". The census taker said "Well if you cannot give me further information I still don't know".

The man said "Well my eldest daughter has a dog with a wooden leg".

The census taker said, "I know now".

What were their ages?

67 What comes next in this series?

1 2 6 24 120 720 –

68 What are X and Y?

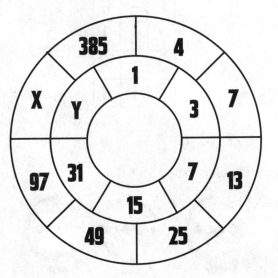

69 What are A, B, C and D?

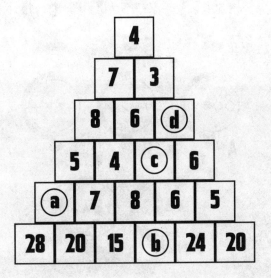

70 Give values for A, B and C?

3	9	**A**
B	2	2
C	5	6
7	8	2
3	5	10
9	1	9

71 Which globe at the bottom belongs to number 6?

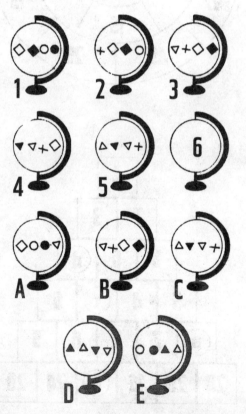

ALIENS

72 100 aliens attended the intergalactic meeting on Earth:

78 had two heads
28 had three eyes
21 had four arms
12 had two heads and three eyes
9 had three eyes and four arms
8 had two heads and four arms
3 had all three unusual features

How many had none of these unusual features?

73 Add the sum of the odd numbers in square A to that of the even numbers in square B and subtract the sum of the prime numbers in square C.

4	7	9
18	26	2
3	5	15

A

8	10	7
3	1	2
14	13	6

B

6	15	17
3	9	4
21	11	19

C

74 What are X and Y?

```
  3 1 X 4
  6 Y 9 5
---------
1 0 0 1 9
```

```
  4 9 1 X
  3 Y 0 1
---------
  1 1 1 1
```

75 Which yacht is the odd one out?

76 Which of these figures is wrong?

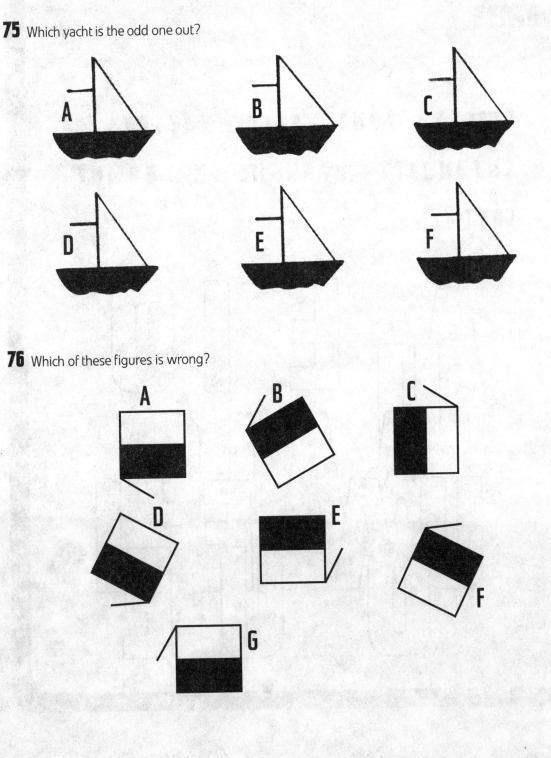

VOWELS

77 All of the vowels have been omitted from this saying. Put them back to produce the saying.

FTFRST   YDNT   SCCD   TRYTRY

GNTHNQTT   HRSNSNS BN   GDMNF

LBTT

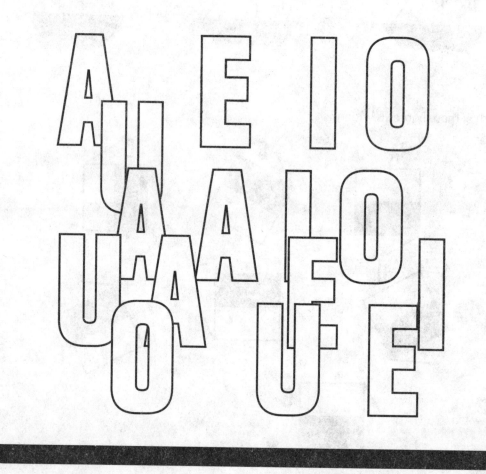

78 Which date does not conform with the others?

A 1584   **B 1692**   **C 1729**   **D 1809**   **E 1980**

79 Who has changed his expression?

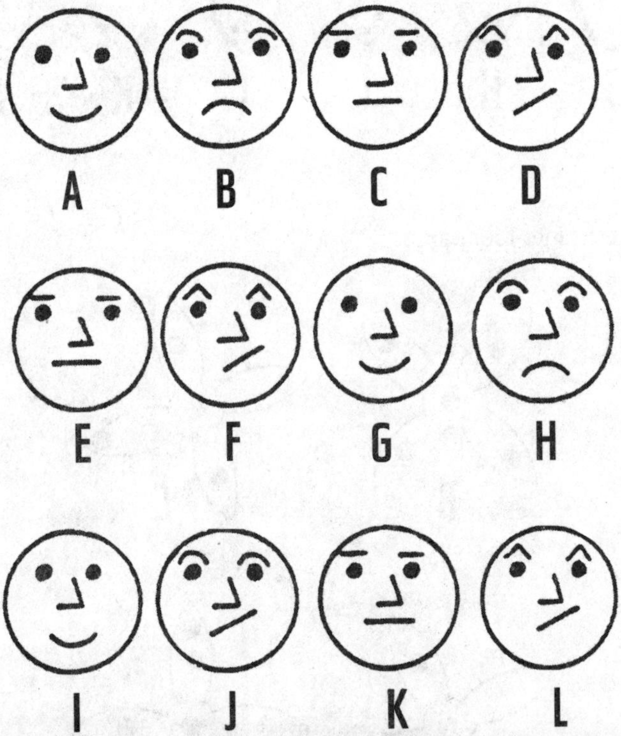

A   B   C   D

E   F   G   H

I   J   K   L

80 What goes into the empty brackets?

144(3625)125

96(1618)126

112(   )144

81 Which two of these shields are identical?

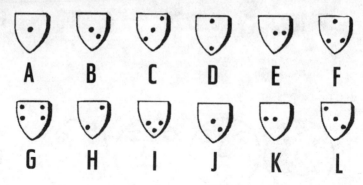

82 Arrange these patterns into four pairs.

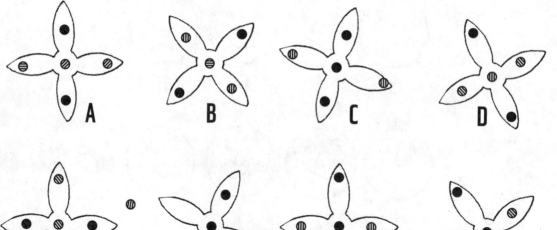

83 Which of these is the odd man out?

4 18 16 8 24

84 Assuming that the two top stars are correct, which of those below are wrong?

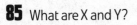

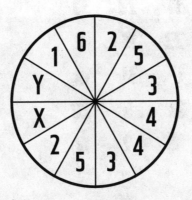

85 What are X and Y?

Puzzles 86-87

86 If is superimposed on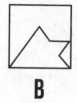

Which of the OUTLINES below will result?

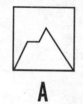

A

B

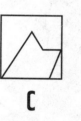

C

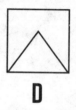

D

87 Which column does not conform?

A	B	C	D	E	F
17	14	22	31	29	33
9	13	15	22	19	8
13	11	17	17	31	19
24	7	2	13	5	20
2	29	8	4	2	17
10	6	21	3	10	3

ZOETROPE

88

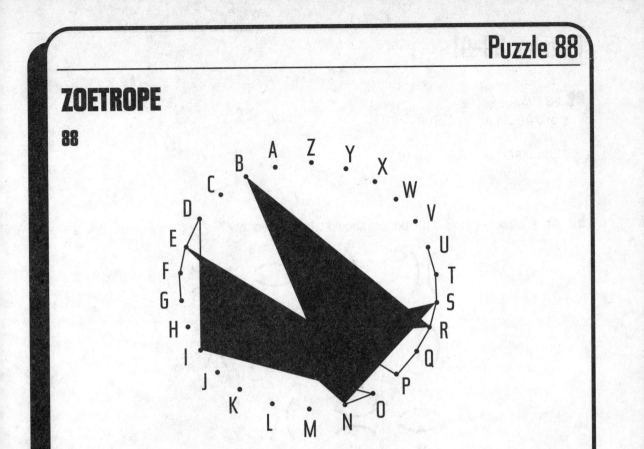

Clue: Hanging about over the water? (10-6)

Find the (10-6) letter word. Find the 1st letter. Draw a straight line to the 2nd letter, then to the 3rd letter and so on. The enclosed areas have been filled in.

89 If 3 (76) equals 212
and 4 (320) equals 125
what is:
5 (6100)?

90 Which of the symbols at the bottom should take the place of X?

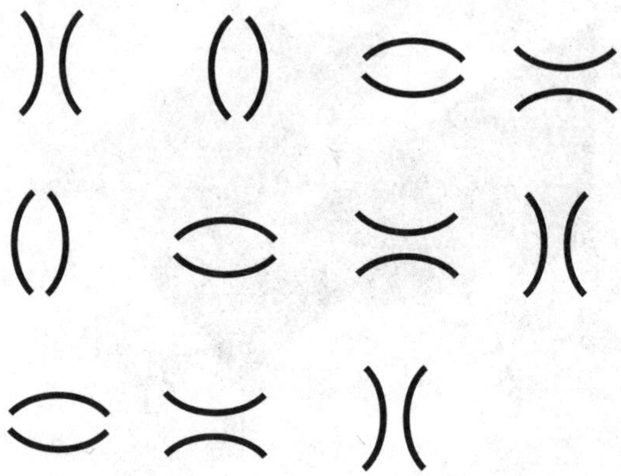

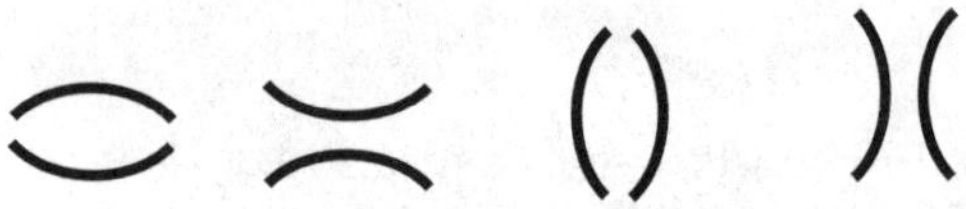

91 What is X?

21859

37262

4211X

92 Arrange these into six pairs:

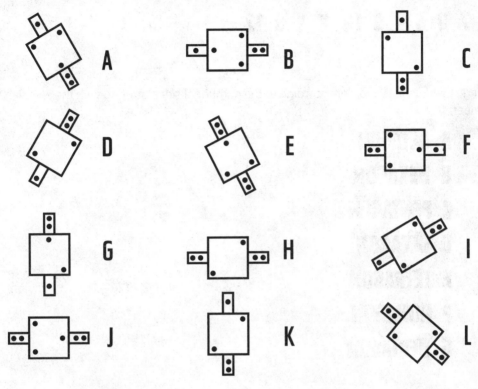

93 Which are the weak links?

94 What are X and Y?

7 8 6 9 5 10 X Y 3 12

95 Arrange these shapes in order according to the number of sides, starting with the one with the least number:

A OCTAGON

B HEXAGON

C PENTAGON

D DECAGON

E TETRAGON

F NONAGON

G HEPTAGON

96 Which cross does not conform with the others?

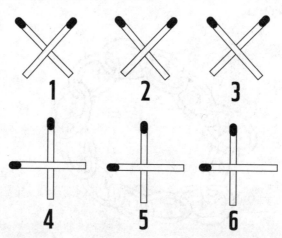

ALPHABET X-WORD

97 Place all of the letters of the alphabet in the grid to make a x-word. 9 letters have been placed for you.

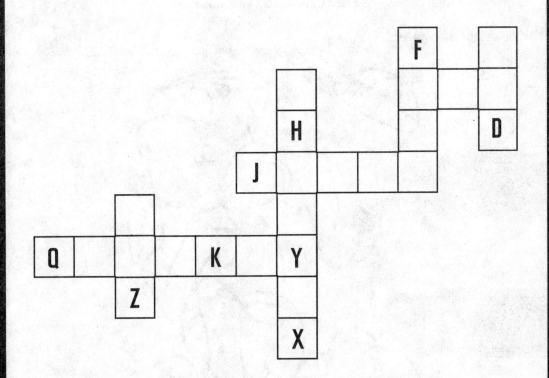

A B C D E F G H I J K L M N
O P Q R S T U V W X Y Z

Puzzle 98

CRICKET

98 The local cricket team used 16 players during the season and each players' total score for the season was a palindromic prime number. No two players had the same score for the season. If you sum the 16 players' total score and then find the average you arrive at a 3-digit number that contains the same 3 digits. The lowest total was 11.

What was the average total?

99 Which envelope should occupy the empty space?

100 Using your eyes only, how many squares are there in the figure below and assuming that A and B were joined, how many triangles?

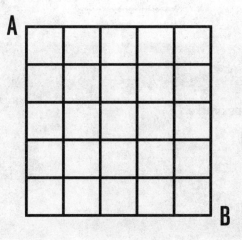

101 Which figure is wrong?

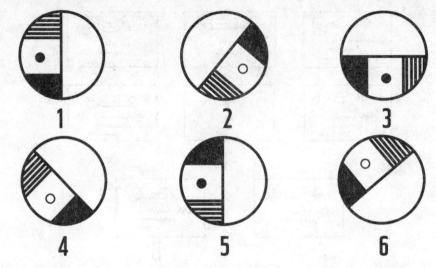

1   2   3

4   5   6

102 What is the value of X in each of the following three diagrams?

5	4	9
3	5	8
2	7	**X**

A

32	35	39
42	46	51
3	8	**X**

B

A	E	J
D	**X**	O
F	L	S

C

103 What number goes into the brackets?

64 (49) 144

85 (57) 119

144 ( ) 90

A GAME OF CRAPS

104 The casino game called craps is played with two dice 1-6 standard.

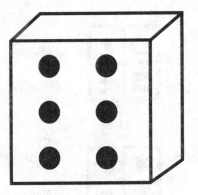 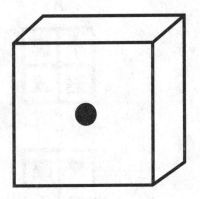

7 or 11 wins.

Which 3 numbers lose?

105 Arrange these patterns into four pairs.

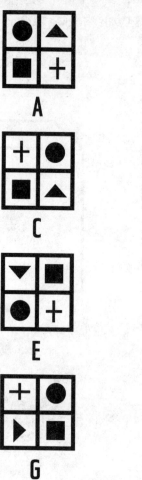
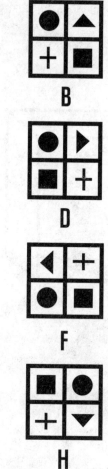

106 Sheffield is 100 miles from Worcester.

At 1pm train A leaves Sheffield for Worcester and travels at a constant speed of 30mph.

One hour later train B leaves Worcester for Sheffield and travels at a constant speed of 40mph.

Each train makes one stop only at a station ten miles form its starting-point and remains there for fifteen minutes.

Which train is nearer to Sheffield when they meet?

107 What two terms complete this series?

A 1 D 4 H 8 M 13 _ _

108 Which of these wrought iron gates differs from the others?

A

B

C

D

109 Which scroll is wrong?

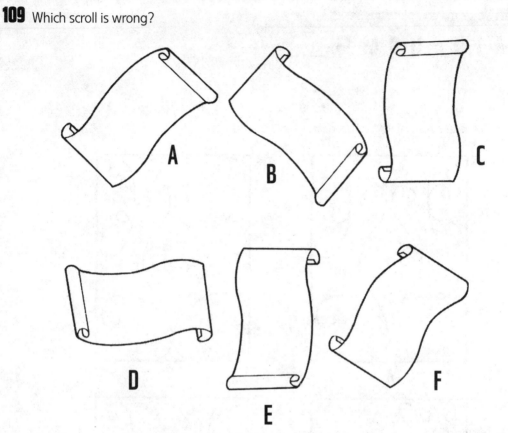

110 Assuming four of these dates are correct, which one is wrong?

A Saturday 7 January 1764

B Saturday 21 January 1764

C Saturday 11 February 1764

D Saturday 11 March 1764

E Saturday 14 April 1764

BOXES

111	Boxes	1 + 2	weigh	12 KG
	"	2 + 3	"	13.5 KG
	"	3 + 4	"	11.5 KG
	"	4 + 5	"	8 KG
	"	1 + 3 + 5	"	16 KG

How much does each box weigh?

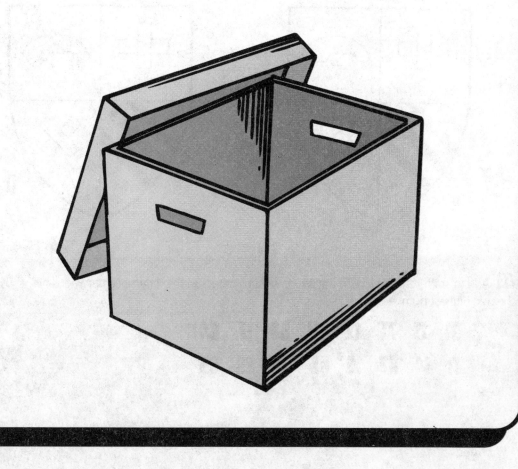

112 Which shield is wrong?

 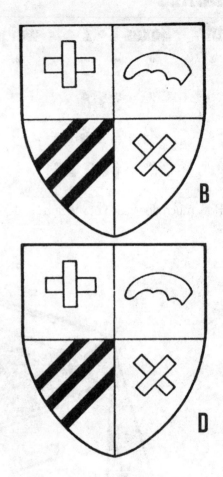

113 Add the difference between the two lowest numbers to the difference between the two highest numbers:

91 13 76 12 7 88 17 84

11 14 87 15 86 16 89 85

114 Subtract the sum of the three lowest numbers from the sum of the three highest numbers.

11	36	7	38	3	45
39	10	48	37	12	36

115 What is the last term in this series?

B 2 T 20 Q 17 G 7 C –

116 What is X ?

4 9 X 25

117 Whose face is wrong?

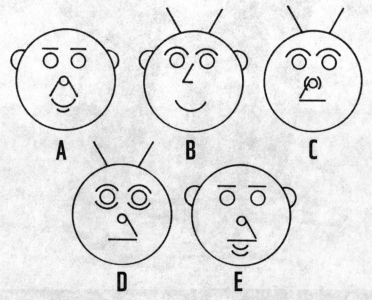

Puzzle 118

ARRESTS

118 At a demonstration, protesters outnumbered the police by 8 to 1. 84 arrests were made, averaging 3 for every 2 policemen.

How many protesters were there?

119 What comes next?

208   CIV   52   XXVI   –

120 Which one does not conform with the others?

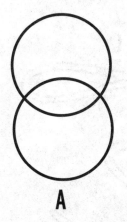

A

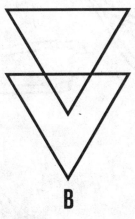

B

C

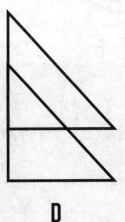

D

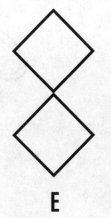

E

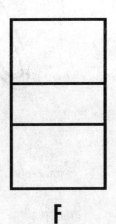

F

121 What knot is different?

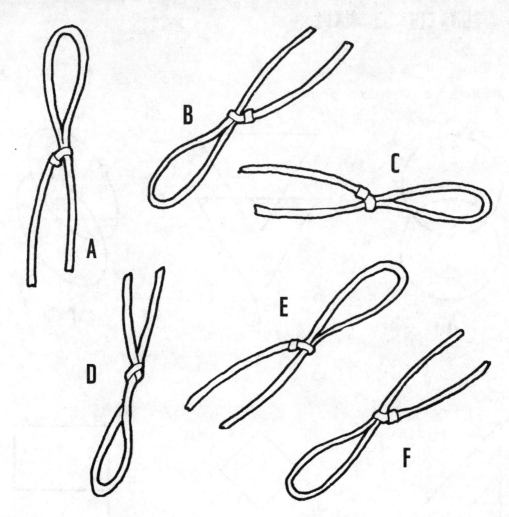

122 If the two figures at the top are correct, which of those below are wrong?

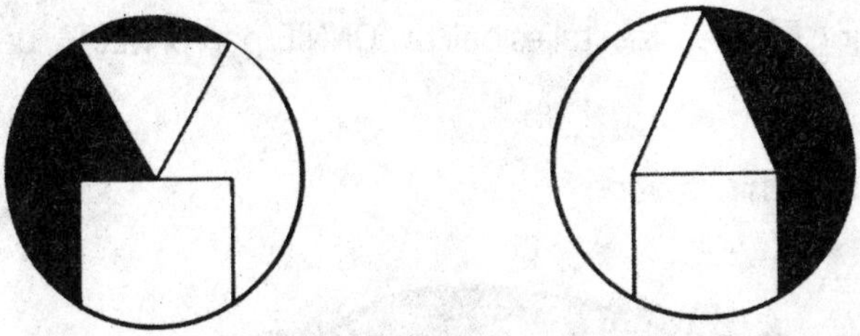

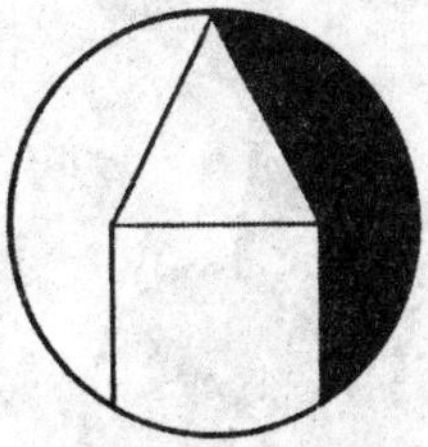

A

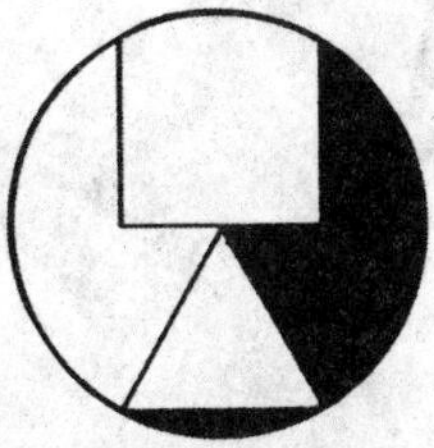

B

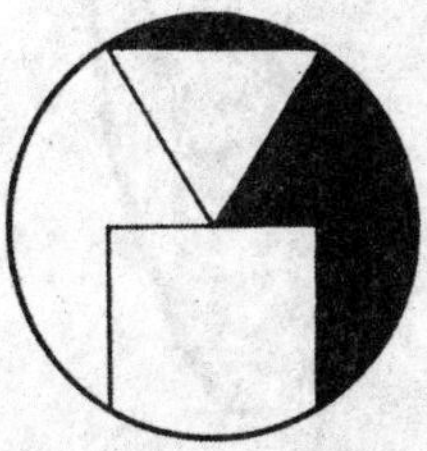

C

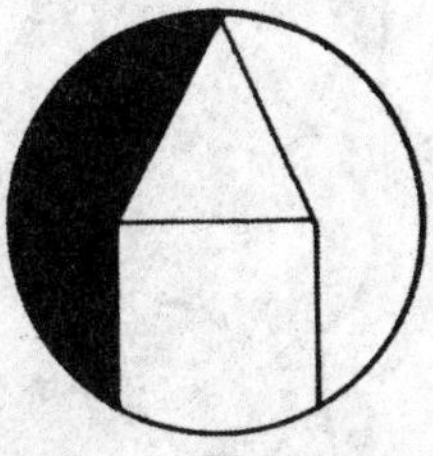

D

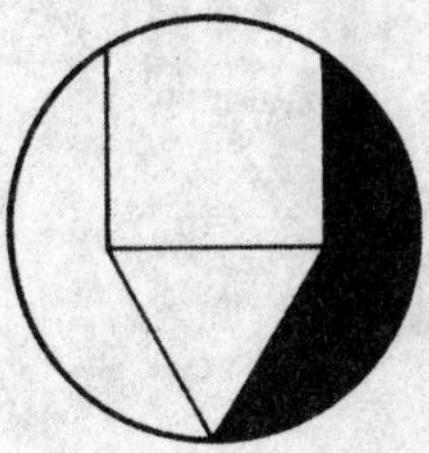

E

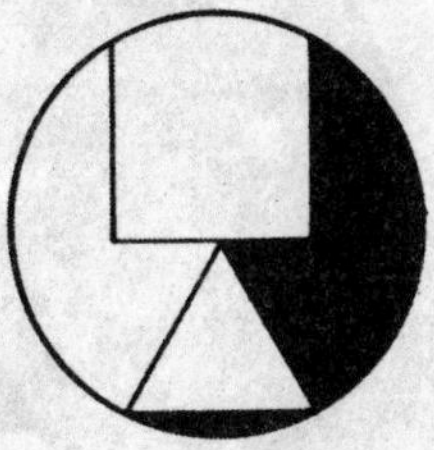

F

Puzzle 123

FRANKENSTEIN

123 For his latest creation Frankenstein takes half of CONNIE, part of NESTA, part of NELLIE, and part of AUNTIE.

What does Frankenstein call his creation?

124 Which of the figures at the bottom belongs to E?

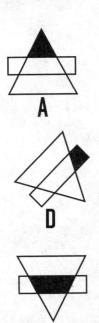

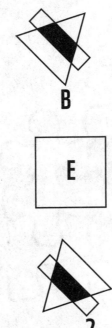

A   B   C

D   E   F

1   2   3

125 Which ladder is wrong?

A   B   C   D   E   F

Puzzle 126

126 Which piece completes the jig-saw puzzle?

127 What numbers should take the place of A & B?

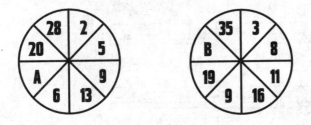

128 Assuming that house A, B, C and D are correct, which of the numbered houses below are incorrect?

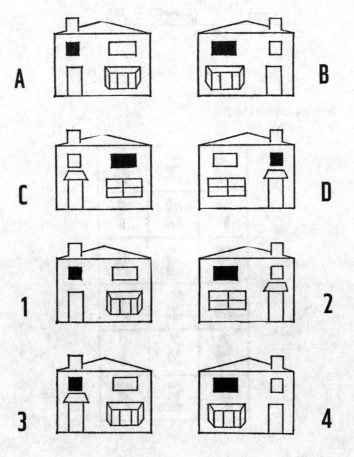

Puzzles 129–130

129 Can you compose music? Study the music below and decide which of the numbered symbols belong to A and B.

130 What numbers are represented by A and B?

4	5	6
7	8	1
5	3	A
B	9	7
9	9	1
7	6	7

ZOETROPE
131

Clue: You need this to run before the wind. (9)

Find the (9) letter word. Find the 1st letter. Draw a straight line to the 2nd letter, then to the 3rd letter and so on. The enclosed areas have been filled in.

132 Complete this sequence:

2 3 4 9 16 81 256

133 How many revolutions of 1 will take place in order to bring the black teeth into mesh with the other:

A If 1 rotates clockwise

B If 2 rotates anti clockwise?

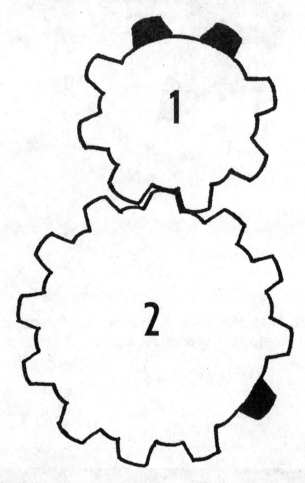

134 What number should replace the question mark?

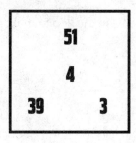

51
4
39   3

71
2
61   5

90
?
24   6

135 A man wagers £40.00 and wins back his original stake, plus £60.00. He spends $\frac{1}{10}$ of it on a meal and $\frac{1}{20}$ of it on a taxi fare home . He then buys a present for his wife which cost $\frac{1}{2}$ of what he had left.

How much more money did he have since he started out?

ALPHABET X-WORD

136 Place all of the letters of the alphabet in the grid to make a crossword.

8 letters have been placed for you.

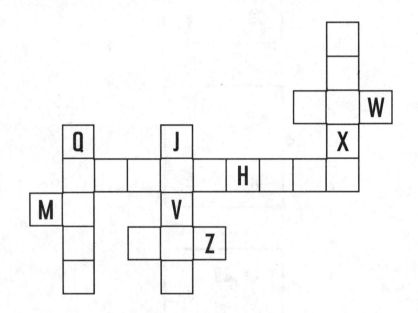

137 The black ball moves one position at a time clockwise. The white ball moves two positions at a time anti-clockwise.

A In how many moves will they be together again?

B In what corner will they be?

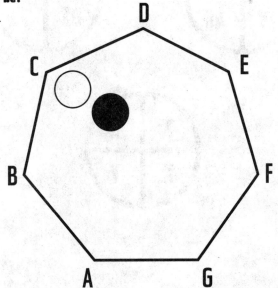

138 What is X?

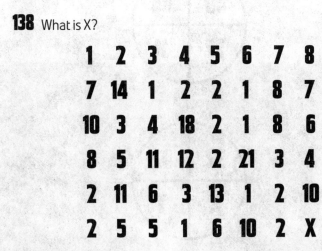

1	2	3	4	5	6	7	8
7	14	1	2	2	1	8	7
10	3	4	18	2	1	8	6
8	5	11	12	2	21	3	4
2	11	6	3	13	1	2	10
2	5	5	1	6	10	2	X

139 What are X and Y?

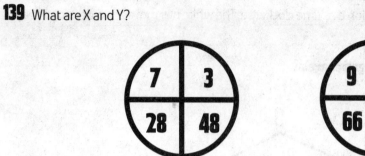

140 What are X and Y?

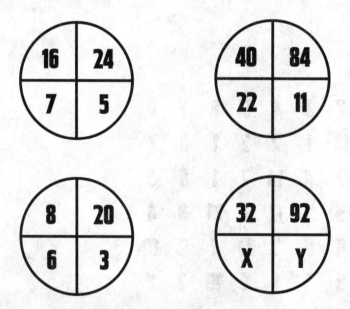

A SIX-HORSE RACE

141 In a 6 horse race the bookmaker needed to make a profit of 25% in order to cover his expenses, salary for his clerk, income tax and profit.

These were the prices, what price should be quoted for No. 6?

Horse No.	Against	
1	2–1	"
2	3–1	"
3	4–1	"
4	5–1	"
5	6–1	"
6	?	"

142 What is X?

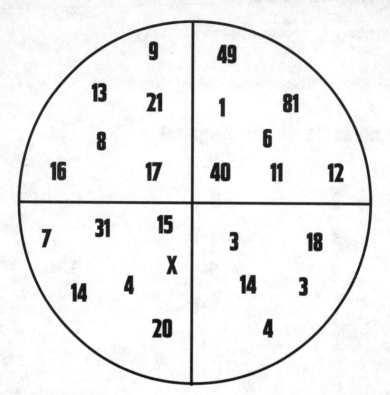

143 If : **4** equals **4**,

9 equals **7 1/2**,

16 equals **12**,

25 equals **17 1/2**,

36 equals **24**,

49 equals **31 1/2**,

What does **64** equal?

144 What word is represented by the seven cards at the bottom?

145 Give the time indicated at X.

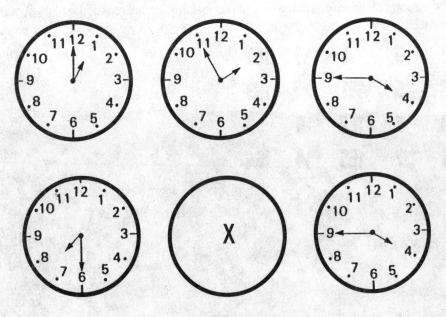

146 Insert arithmetical signs between these numbers to make the equation correct:

18 2 9 24 5 = 100

147 Which is the odd one out?

A.	K	N	Q	T	W	Z
B.	B	F	J	N	R	V
C.	A	F	K	P	V	Z
D.	3	6	9	12	15	18
E.	7	11	15	19	23	27
F.	13	18	23	28	33	38

148 What is the total of the square of the lowest number, the square root of the highest number, and the number that is midway between the results?

168	9	4	167	162
8	5	161	7	163
169	6	166	10	3
11	12	165	14	164

PLAYING FIELD

149 The grass in a school playing field had to be cut.
One man could mow the grass in 4 hours
One man could mow the grass in 5 hours
One man could mow the grass in 6 hours
One man could mow the grass in 8 hours

If they all joined forces to cut the field and they all worked at their individual rates, how long would it take to cut the grass?

Puzzle 150

CLOTH

150 A factory was cutting rolls of cloth into 1 metre lengths, from a 200 metre roll. How long would it take for the machine to cut the roll if each cut took 4 secs?

151 The black blocks each weigh 3 kilograms. The white blocks each weigh 2 kilograms. which of these see-saws is wrong?

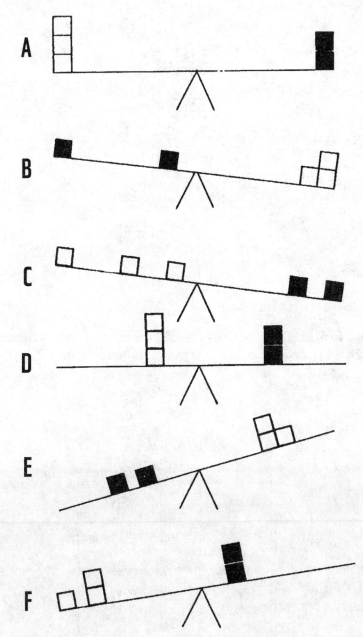

152 Think of the numbers from 1 to 10 and decide which domino is missing:

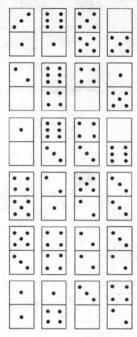

153 Given that the area of a circle is 3.14 times the square of its radius, and without using a pocket calculator, which of the figures below has an area nearest to that of the circle?

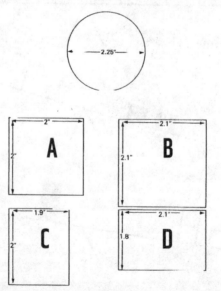

CHILDREN

154 A woman has 7 children.

On multiplying their ages together one obtains the number 6591.

Given that today is the birthday of all 7, what are their seven ages? There are two sets of triplets.

155 Match these into four pairs:

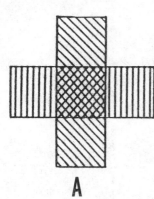

A

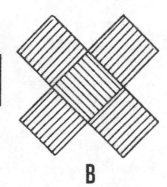

B

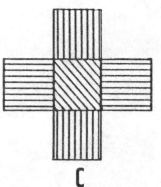

C

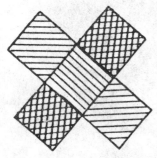

D

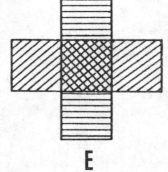

E

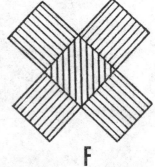

F

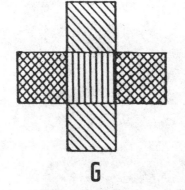

G

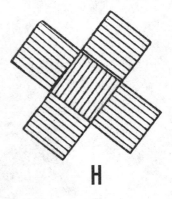

H

156 Which triangle is the odd one out?

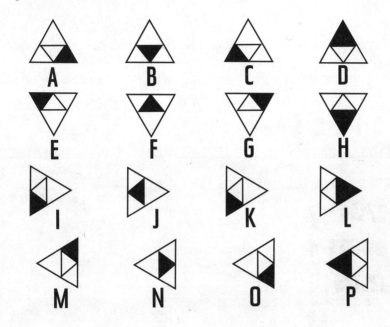

157 Which two pieces will make the hexagon?

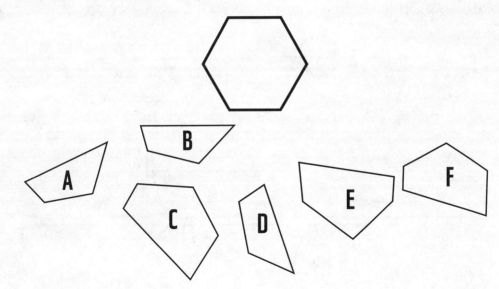

158 When the die shows an even number on top, the counter moves two places forward in addition to the number on the die.

When the die shows an odd number on top, the counter moves one place back in addition to the number on the die.

On what number will the counter be after seven throws of the die, producing the following numbers on top.

6 4 3 1 2 6 5

159 What goes into the empty brackets?

12 (27144) 3

13 (64169) 4

14 (125196) 5

15 (   ) 6

160 Which key will not fit the lock?

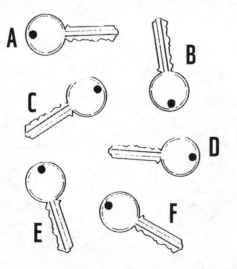

161 What number should replace the question mark to a definite rule?

147   **159**   **174**   **186**   **?**

162 A farmer told his labourer to pick 896,809 apples and pack them into as few boxes as possible, each having the same number of apples.
How many boxes did he use?

163 Which of these is the odd one out?

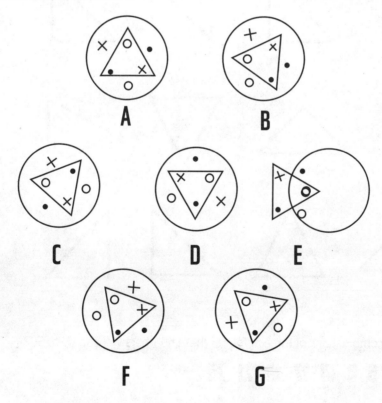

A

B

C

D

E

F

G

164 A driving school claims an average test pass rate of 76.8 per cent. What is the least number of pupils required to achieve this result?

165 Which row does not conform with the others?

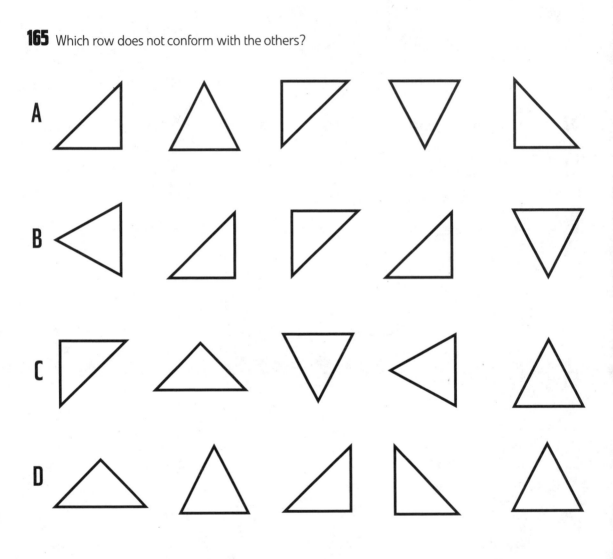

A

B

C

D

166 How many combinations of three or four of these numbers will add up to 50?

2 4 6 8 10 17 19 21 25

ENVELOPES

167 A correspondent writes 7 letters and addresses 7 envelopes, one for each letter. In how many ways can all of the letters be placed in the wrong envelopes?

ALPHAMETICS

168 Replace the letters with numbers.

```
      COPS
     CLOSE
    CELLAR
    CORPSE
      CASE
  +  COLLAR
    RECTOR
```

169

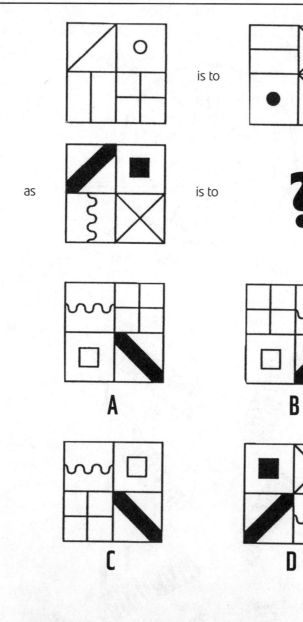

is to

as

is to

?

A   B

C   D

170 Which number in the bottom line comes next in the top line?

9   8   10   18   21   16   –

14   15   20   27

171 Give values for X and Y.

172 Which is the odd one out?

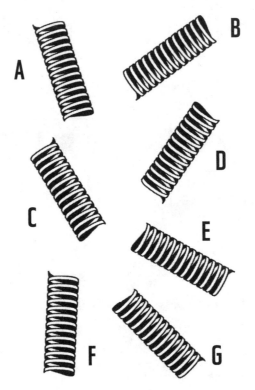

173 What comes next in this series?

1 7 8 15 23 38 61 –

174 Which is the odd one out?

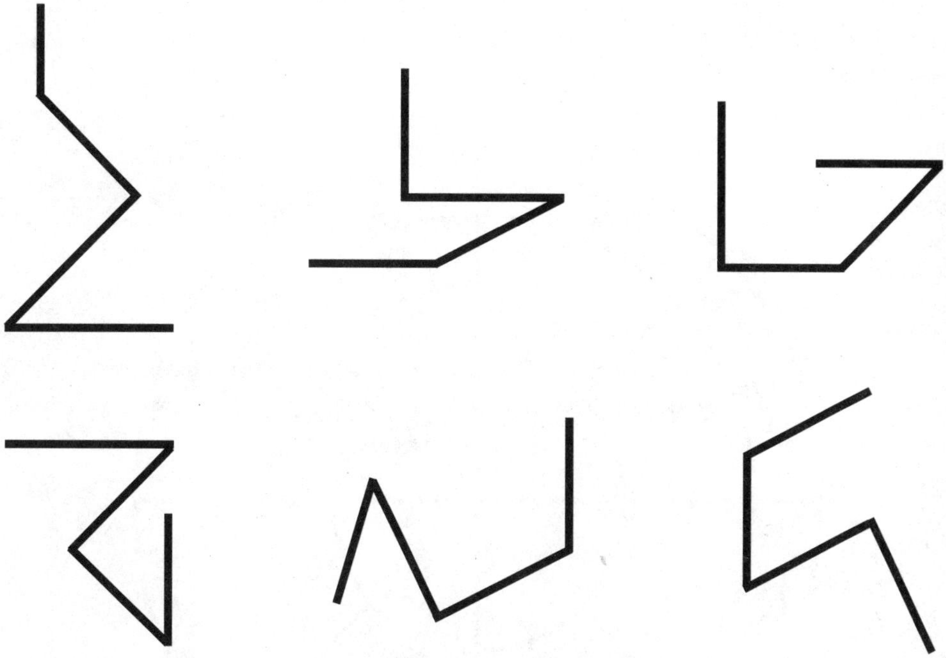

175 What number goes into the empty brackets?

98 (79) 126
105 (79) 135
48 (35) 80
34 (   ) 85

176 What are A, B and C?

$$
\begin{array}{cccc}
  & 3 & A & 6 \\
  & C & 4 & B \\
\hline
B & 2 & B & A \\
\end{array}
$$

177 What is X?

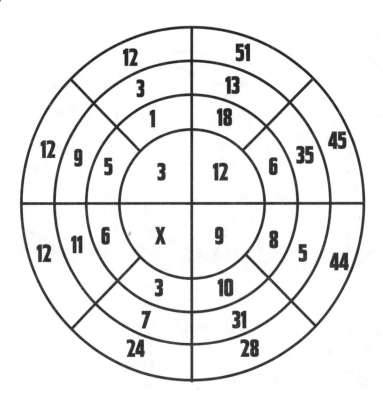

178 What is X?

25 22 15 X 10 19 24

HIGH SCHOOL REUNION

179 Barbara visited her High School friend, Natasha after their 25th school reunion. "What a nice pair of children you have, are they twins?", Barbara asked.

"No my sister is older than I", said Natasha's son Philip. "The square of my age plus the cube of her age is 7148".

"The square of my age plus the cube of his age is 5274", said Matilda.

How old were they?

Puzzle 180

A PASSING MOVE

180 A train moving at 49 mph meets and is passed by a train moving at 63 mph. A passenger in the first train noted that the second train took 4.5 seconds to pass him. How long is the second train?

181 Group these symbols into five sets of three.

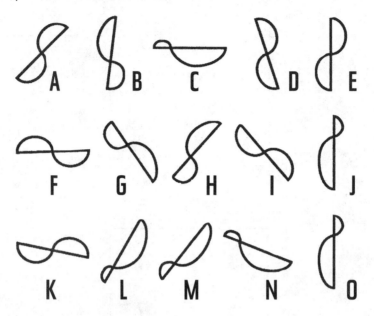

182 Group these six figures into three pairs.

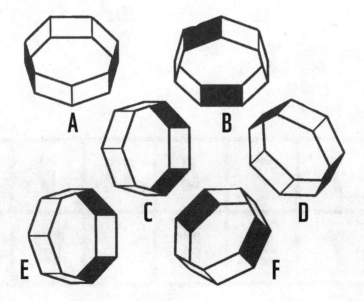

183 Multiply the numbers that are midway between the lowest and highest numbers in A and B and subtract the midway number in C.

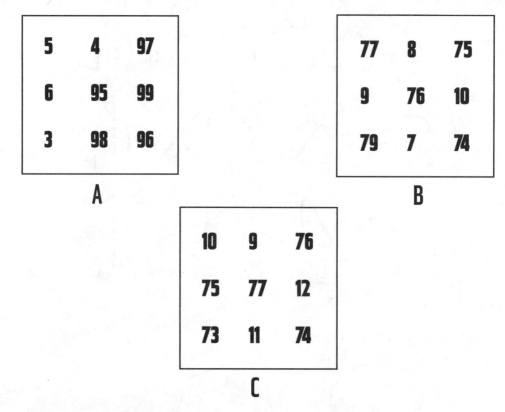

184 What goes into the empty square?

0	7	2	4	12	6	3
	7	9	6			18	9

JEWELS

185 The 1st man has 16 sapphires
The 2nd man has 10 emeralds
The 3rd man has 8 diamonds

Each man gives the other two, two of his gems and then all 3 have the same value of wealth.

What are the individual values of the three types of jewels?

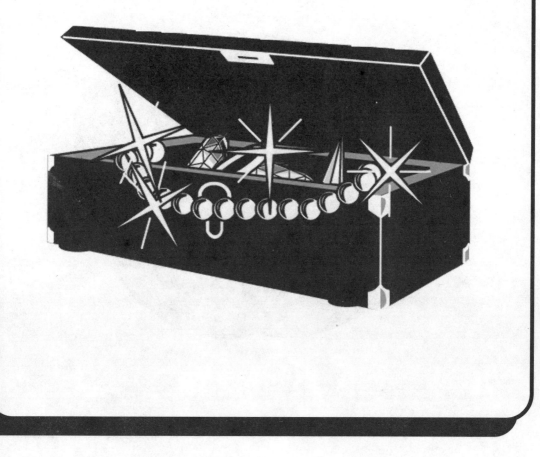

Puzzle 186

APPLES

186 A man had to pack apples in packets, but as each packet has to have exactly the same number of apples, he was having difficulty.

If he packed 10 apples in a packet, one packet had only 9
      "   9   "   "   8
      "   8   "   "   7
      "   7   "   "   6
and so on, down to
      "   2   "   "   1

How many apples did he have?

187 Which is the odd one out?

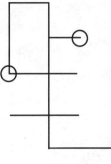

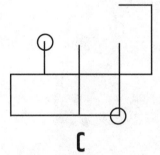

A

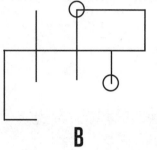

B

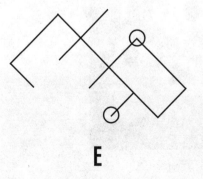

C

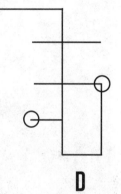

D

E

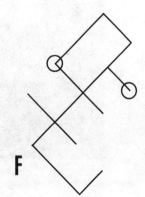

F

Puzzle 188

KEYS

188 The porter had mixed up the room keys. There are 20 rooms. What is the maximum number of trials required to sort out the keys?

ZOETROPE

189

Clue: Spindrift skimmers! (4-7)

Find the (4-7) letter words. Find the 1st letter. Draw a straight line to the 2nd letter, then to the 3rd letter and so on. The enclosed areas have been filled in.

190 Which hexagon fits the missing space?

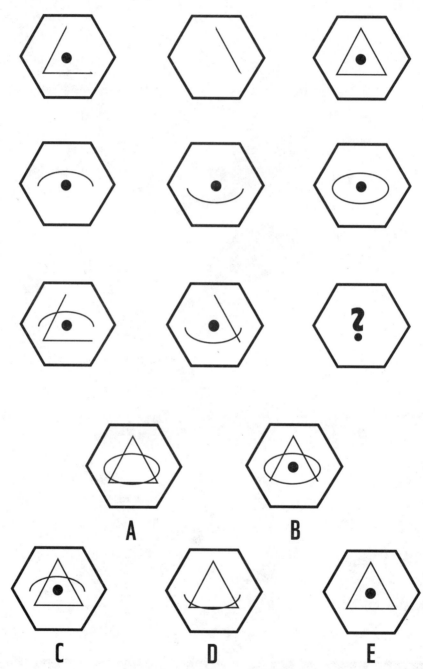

191 If the two figures at the top are correct, which of those below are wrong?

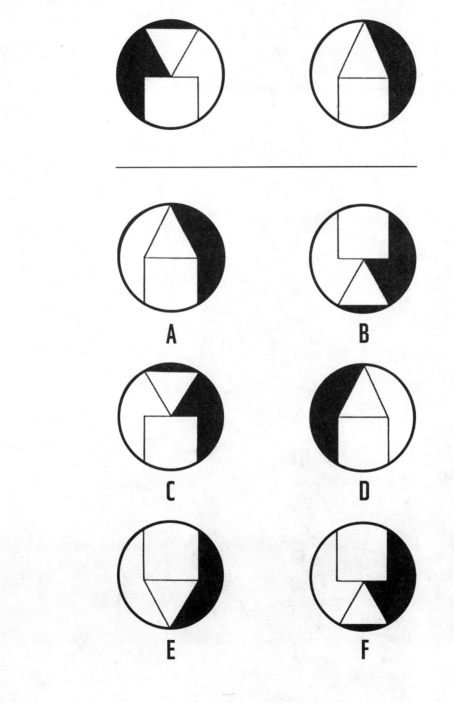

192 Which one is wrong?

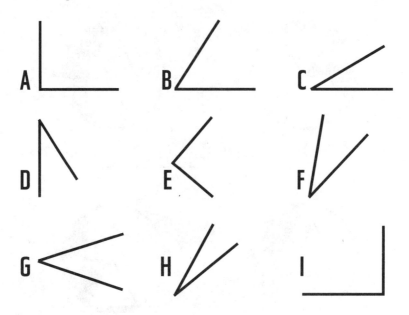

193 Which tumbler is wrong?

ALPHAMETICS

194 Replace the letters with numbers.

```
    TWELVE
    TWELVE
    TWELVE
    TWELVE
    TWELVE
  + THIRTY
   ─────────
    NINETY
   ─────────
```

195 What are X and Y?

S	20
8	J
W	25
16	T
A	4
5	K
C	7
X	L
A	Y
4	N

196 A rotates clockwise all the time, one position at a time. If it stops on an odd number, ball B moves one place anti-clockwise; if A stops on an even number, B moves three places clockwise. If ball B stops on an even number, ball C moves three places clockwise; if B stops on an odd number, C moves five places anti-clockwise.

At the end of six moves what place will be spelled out by ball C?

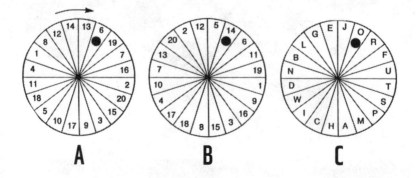

197 Assuming that the top two houses are correct, which of those below are wrong?

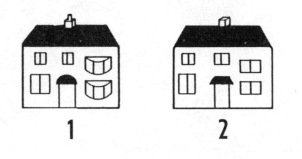

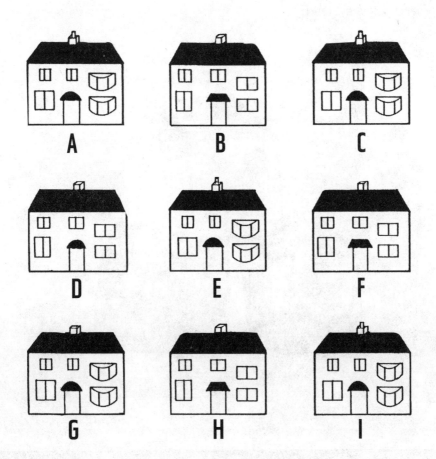

BLOCKS

198 I have 11 blocks

4 of them are 8" thick
2 of them are 4" thick
3 of them are 3" thick
2 of them are 1" thick

Pile them in a column 51" high with a 3" block at the bottom so that individual blocks or combinations of adjacent blocks can be used to measure every thickness in exact inches from 1" to 48".

In which order should they stand?

REBUS

199 Solve the rebus.

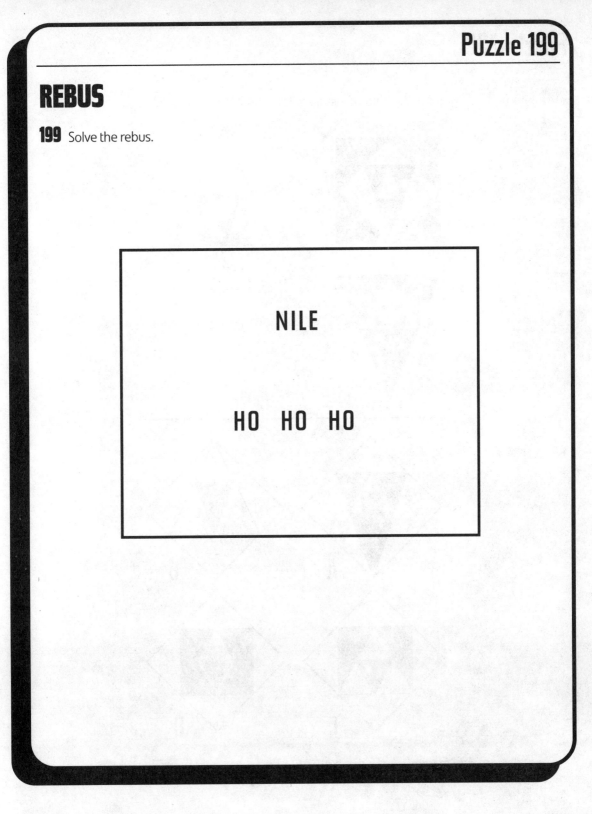

Puzzle 200

200 Which of the figures at the bottom should follow number 3 at the top?

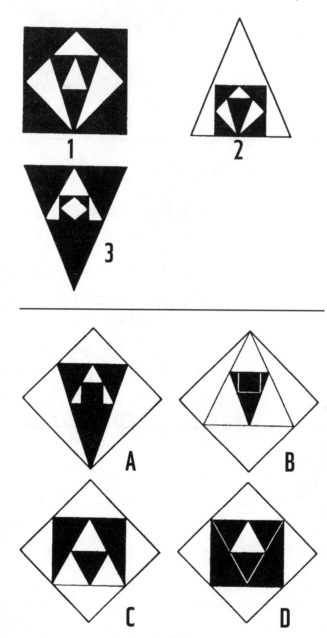

201 What is X?

4 9 1 3 2 2 3 5 5 7 9 X

202 Here is part of a jigsaw puzzle on which a triangle is marked. Which is the missing piece?

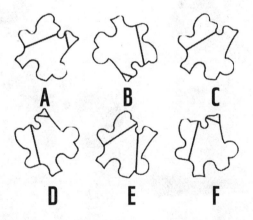

203 What number goes into the empty brackets?

916 (160) 916

971 (177) 879

245 (   ) 511

204 What comes between 16 and 4 in this series?

6561   **256**   **81**   **16**   **–**   **4**   **3**

205 Six of these keys will open the door. Which one won't?

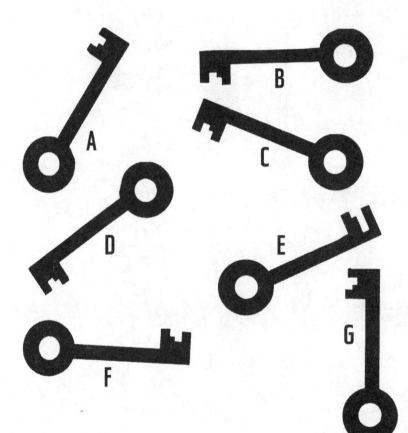

206 Pair these words to make nine titles of books by Charles Dickens:

A	LITTLE		1	RUDGE
B	PICKWICK		2	COPPERFIELD
C	EDWIN		3	TIMES
D	BARNABY		4	CHUZZLEWIT
E	NICHOLAS		5	PAPERS
F	HARD		6	HOUSE
G	BLEAK		7	DROOD
H	DAVID		8	DORRIT
I	MARTIN		9	NICKLEBY

207 Which screw is different?

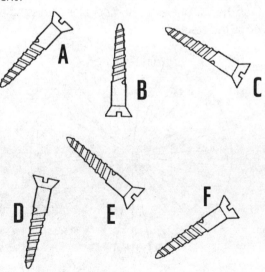

208 Which of the figures below should occupy the vacant space?

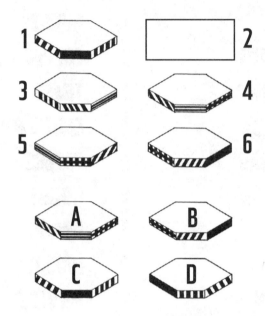

209 Here is a roulette wheel. When the ball stops at zero all the stakes go to the casino. The ball travels anti-clockwise. At the first spin it stops at the next number. Then it misses one and stops at the next. After that each spin brings the ball one extra number along (missing two, then three, and so on). At what spin will the stakes go to the casino?

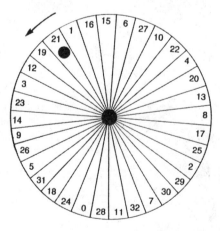

210 Arrange these into four pairs.

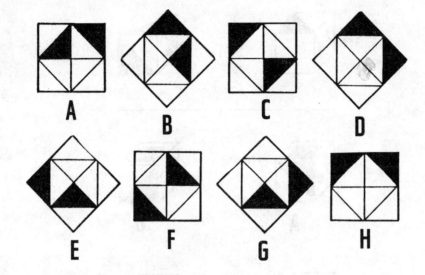

211 What goes into the empty space?

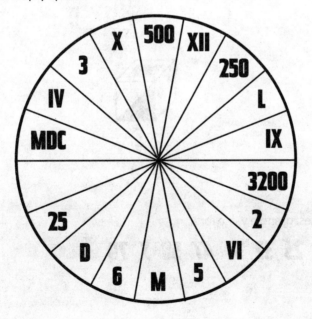

212 Which of the cubes at the bottom should follow the two at the top?

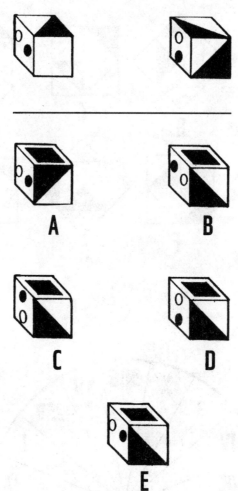

213 Complete this series, giving a value for X.

11 13 17 25 32 37 47 58 X 79

214 If A **were placed** on top of B **which** of the outlines below would result?

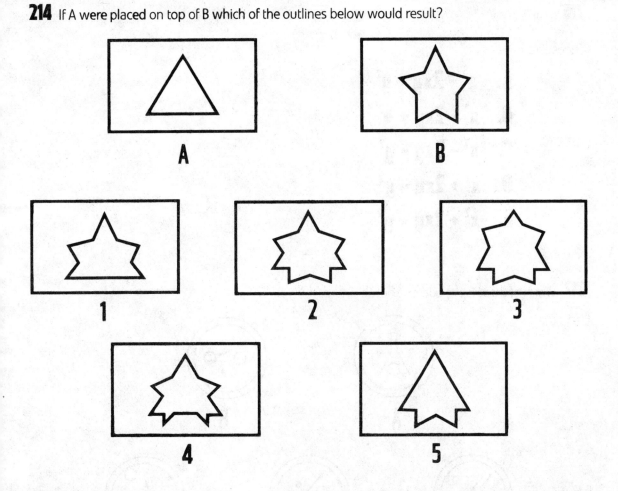

215 What number should replace the question mark?

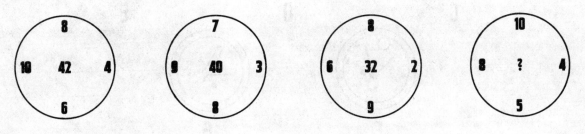

216 Simplify $(x-y)^2$

Choose from

A. $-x^2 - 2xy + y^2$

B. $x^2 - 2xy + y^2$

C. $x^2 - 2xy - y^2$

D. $x^2 + 2xy - y^2$

E. $-x^2 + 2xy + y^2$

217 Which of these is the odd one out?

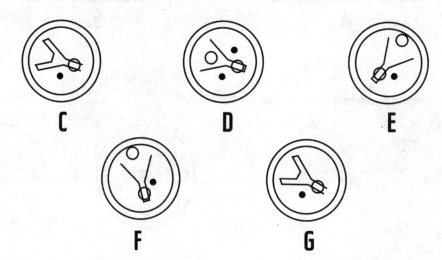

A   **B**

C   **D**   **E**

F   **G**

218 What number comes next in this sequence?

1 8 70 627 5639 ?

219 Which figure is the odd one out?

A

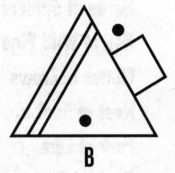

B

C

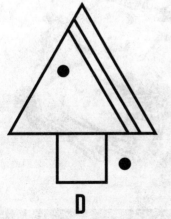

D

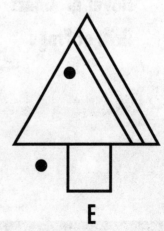

E

Puzzle 220

ALL MIXED UP

220 These are the recognised names given to groups of creatures, but they have been mixed up. You have to re-arrange them correctly.

Colony of Birds
Horde of Spiders
Den of Wild Pigs
Clutter of Crows
Nest of Snakes
Park of Elks
Doylt of Ferrets
Gang of Machine Guns
Business of Swine
Volery of Artillery
Hover of Gnats
Drift of Frogs

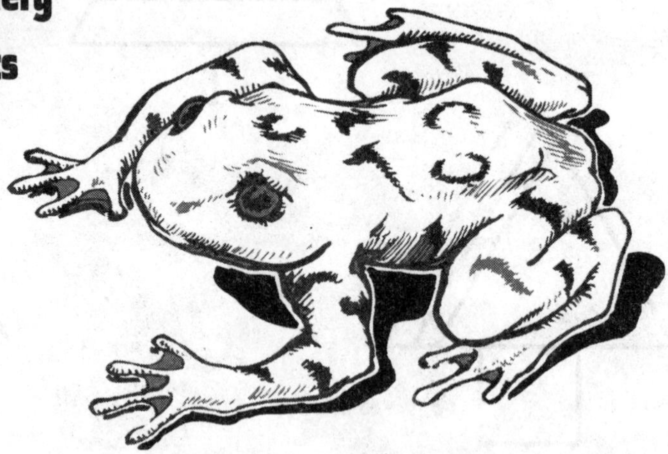

221 You don't have to be a motorist to solve this. Minimum stopping distances are as follows:

at 20mph ... 40 feet

at 30mph ... 75 feet

at 40mph ... 120 feet

at 50mph ... 175 feet

at 60mph ... 240 feet

at 70mph ... 315 feet

When following another vehicle a gap of one yard (three feet) for every mile per hour MAY be sufficient.

At what speed would this gap exactly correspond with the minimum stopping distance?

222 What is the total of the spots on the rear sides of these dice?

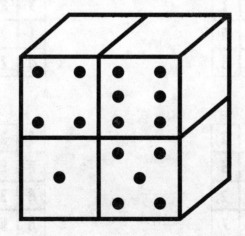

223 Which of the four squares at the bottom should follow square 4?

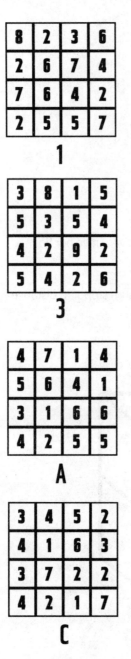

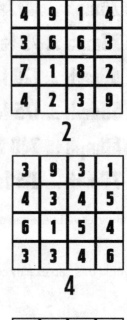

8	2	3	6
2	6	7	4
7	6	4	2
2	5	5	7

1

4	9	1	4
3	6	6	3
7	1	8	2
4	2	3	9

2

3	8	1	5
5	3	5	4
4	2	9	2
5	4	2	6

3

3	9	3	1
4	3	4	5
6	1	5	4
3	3	4	6

4

4	7	1	4
5	6	4	1
3	1	6	6
4	2	5	5

A

7	1	4	3
3	8	2	2
1	4	4	6
4	2	5	4

B

3	4	5	2
4	1	6	3
3	7	2	2
4	2	1	7

C

1	2	7	7
8	6	1	2
4	3	5	5
4	6	4	3

D

ALPHABET X-WORD

224 Place the 26 letters of the alphabet into the grid to make a x-word.

7 letters have already been placed for you.

A B C D E F G H I J K L M N
O P Q R S T U V W X Y Z

BIRTHDAYS

225 If there were twenty-four people in a room and you bet that at least one coincidence of birth dates existed would you have a better chance of winning or losing your bet?

226 Using the example set in the top grid, what are X and Y in the bottom grid?

6	7	■	3	9	3
■	6	6	3	■	7
6	■	2	4	6	5
2	4	5	7	1	■
5	9	1	■	8	5
4	■	5		2	■

4	1	4	8	■	6
■	11	2	■	6	7
3	3	X	7	1	■
■	■	3	Y	8	2
2	9	5	1	■	7
■	4	■	5	4	6

227 What is X in the last circle?

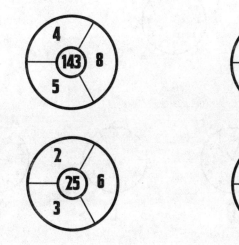

228 Which of the clocks at the bottom should take the place of the last one in those above?

A B C D

BATH

229 You have left out the plug in the bath, and you are filling the bath with both taps on.

The hot tap takes 6 minutes to fill the bath.

The cold tap takes 4 minutes to fill the bath.

The bath empties in 12 minutes.

In how many minutes will the bath be filled?

BUTCHER

230 A butcher had a number of legs of lamb to chop up. He chopped each leg into 11 pieces. He chopped at the rate of 45 strokes per minute. How many legs would he chop in 22 mins?

231 Simplify:

$$\frac{11}{12} \div \frac{33}{48} = X$$

232 What circle should replace the question mark?

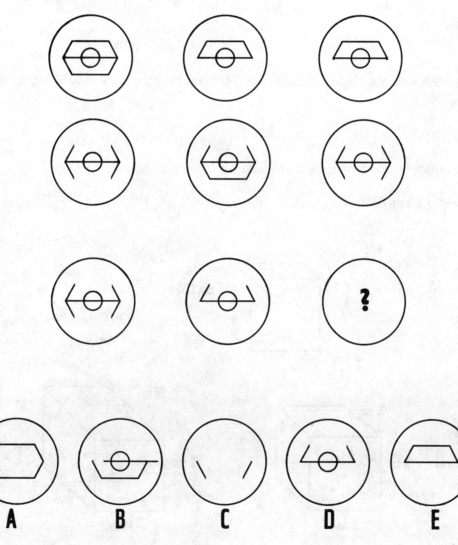

233 What number should replace the question mark?

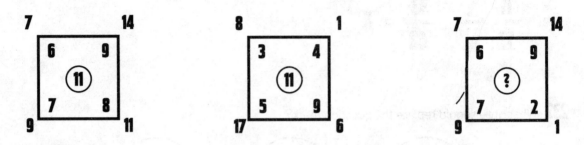

234 If a stone is dropped from a cliff and takes 5 seconds to hit the water, how high is the cliff?

235 How many boxes 2.5 cm cube can be placed in these three boxes?

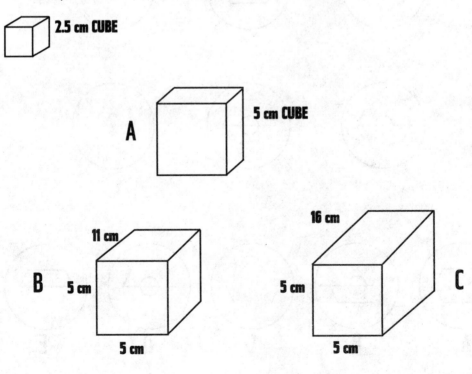

236 Which of the circles at the bottom should take the place of X?

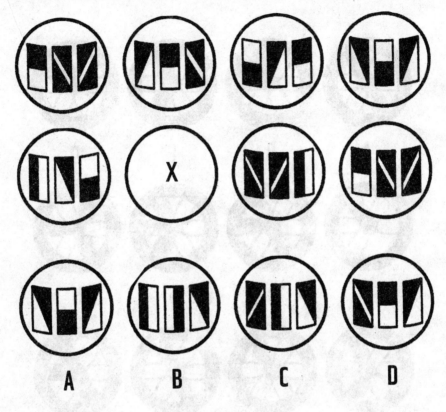

237 Which bar code is wrong?

238 Match these into eight pairs.

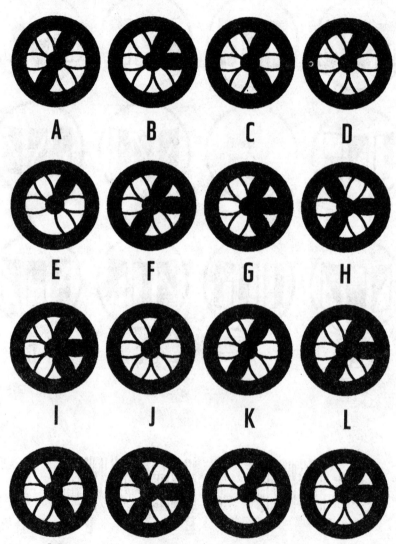

239 Multiply the highest prime numbers by the lowest even number and subtract the result from the total of the numbers remaining.

14 20 13 7 16 11 3 10 17 18 8 12 5 6

240 Which circle has been drawn by the compass? (Do not use any artificial guides.)

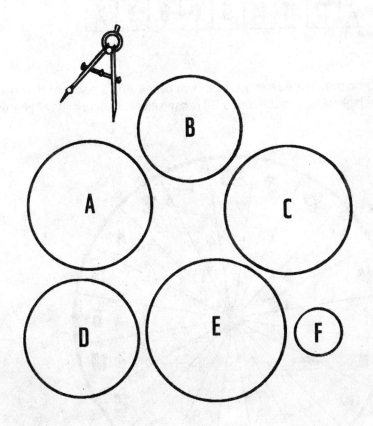

241 What is x?

4	7	9	11	8	15	21	6	5
7	6	1	19	11	7	17	8	4
3	11	15	2	9	8	13	10	9
15	8	3	10	4	9	1	3	9
3	13	10	5	1	10	1	6	19
2	12	11	14	5	6	8	3	X

242 The numbers on the dartboard are arranged as shown below. Add the sum of 10 consecutive numbers that will give the highest total to the sum of 10 consecutive numbers that will give the lowest total.

The Door Number Puzzle

243 Two workmen, Bob and Frank, were putting the finishing touches to a new door they had fitted to house number 7461. All that was left to do was screw the four metal digits to the door.

"Here's a puzzle for you", said Bob, "is it possible to screw these four digits on the door in such a way that the four-figure number thus produced cannot be divided by 9 exactly, without leaving a remainder?"

"I don't even have to think about that one", said Frank, "It simply is not possible".

Why did he reply so quickly, and was he correct?

Puzzle 244

Scratch Card

244 At a local fund raising effort our local Rotary Club ran a competition where each person who donated received a card with a number of rub-off pictures.

Just one picture has on it the Devil's Head, and only four pictures are identical.

If the four pictures which are identical appear before the Devil's Head appears, then the competitor wins a prize. If, however, the Devil's head is uncovered, then the competitor loses.

There were a total of 35 pictures on the card.

What are the chances of winning?

245 Which is the odd one out?

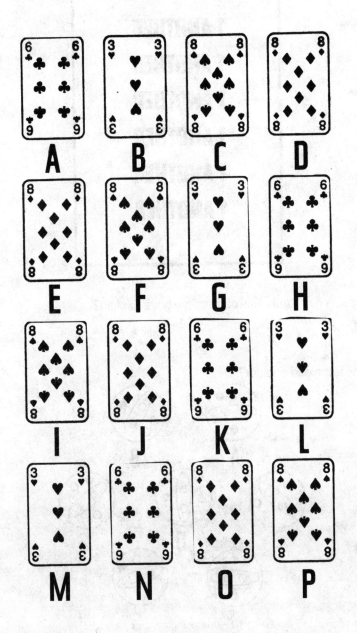

246 What does this rectangle mean?

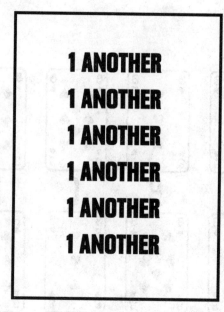

1 ANOTHER
1 ANOTHER
1 ANOTHER
1 ANOTHER
1 ANOTHER
1 ANOTHER

247 A woman has seven children. Half of them are boys. Explain?

248 Which of these is the odd one out?

A   B

C   D   E

F   G

249 (i) Which globe in the second line should be placed at X?

(ii) Which globe in the bottom line should be placed at Y?

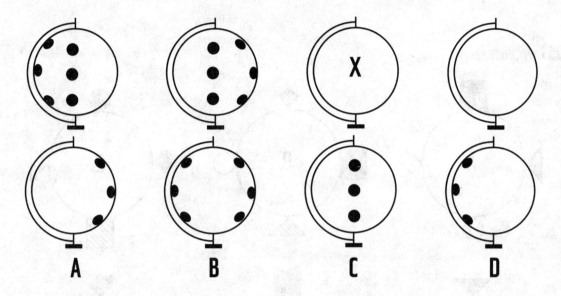

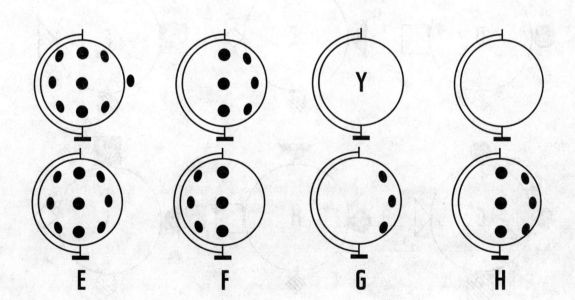

250 Complete this sequence:

$$7 \quad 91 \quad 11 \quad 143 \quad 16 \quad 208 \quad - \quad -$$

251 Which figure is wrong?

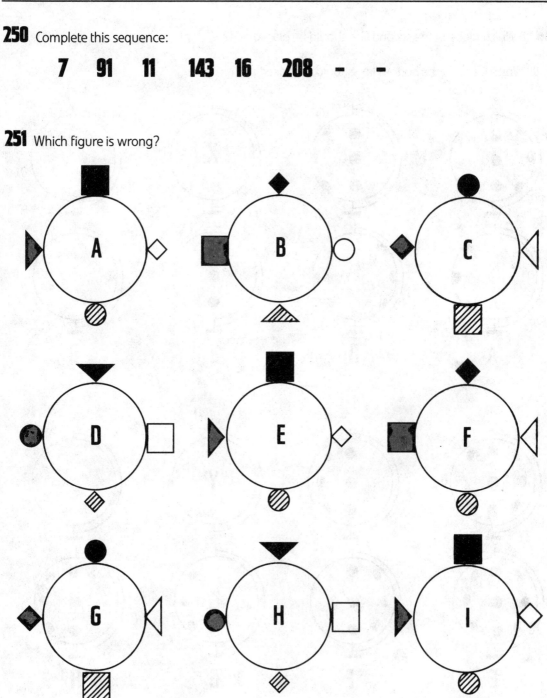

252 Which shape will complete the hexagon?

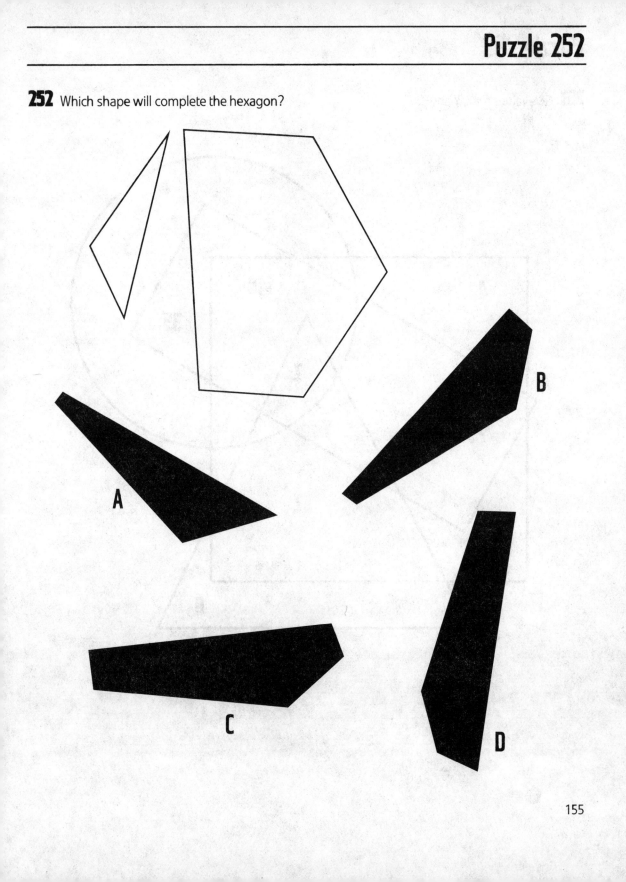

253 Give values for X, Y and Z.

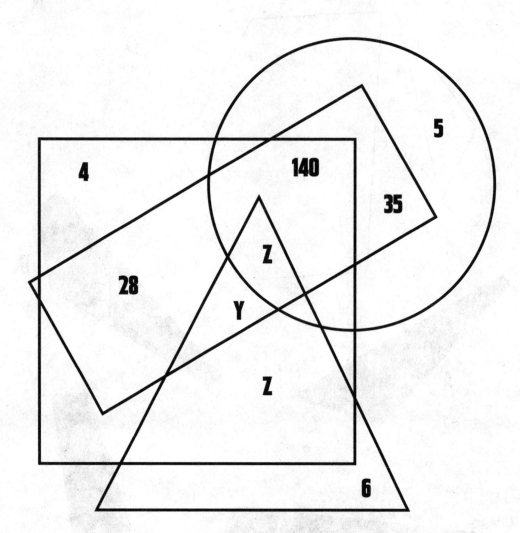

254 This octagonal-shaped figure has its faces numbered consecutively from 1-8.

Imagine that it is turned anti-clockwise.
In the first move its position is changed by one face, in the second move by two faces, in the third move by three faces, and so on.

At the end of EIGHT moves what number will be in the present position of number 1?

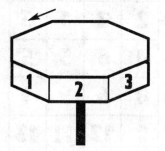

255 Which is the odd face out?

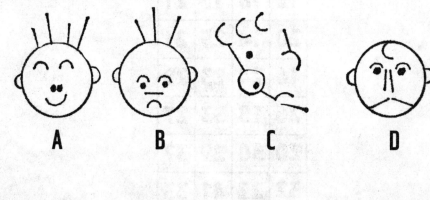

A   B   C   D

E   F   G   H

Crazy Columns

256 These columns are indeed crazy, and at first glance there does not appear to be rhyme nor reason in the way the numbers are distributed.

However, on closer inspection can you see a pattern emerging, and can you fill in the bottom row of numbers?

2	2	1	3
4	6	5	5
8	6	9	9
8	12	11	13
14	10	17	15
12	18	17	21
20	14	25	21
16	24	23	29
26	18	33	27
20	30	29	37
32	22	41	33
24	36	35	45
38	26	49	39
?	?	?	?

257 Which one does not conform?

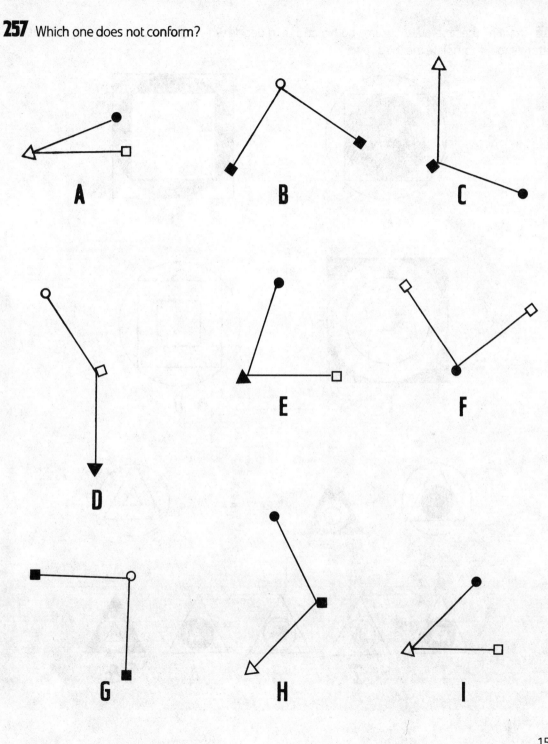

A

B

C

D

E

F

G

H

I

Puzzle 258

258 Examine the first four diagrams below and then decide which of the numbered diagrams at the bottom should complete the third row.

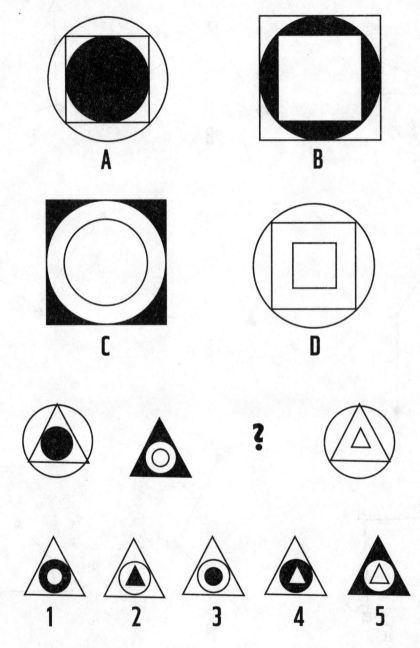

259 Which numbers belong to X, Y and Z?

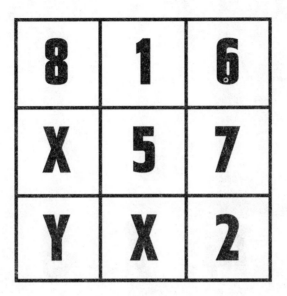

8	1	6
X	5	7
Y	X	2

260 What is the next number in this sequence?

1   3   8   19   42   89   –

261 What number goes into the empty square?

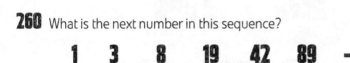

0	4	5	8	7	1	3
	4	9	13		8	4

262 What number is missing in this sequence?

4   16   8   64   32   –   512

263 Which of the numbered symbols at the bottom belongs to x?

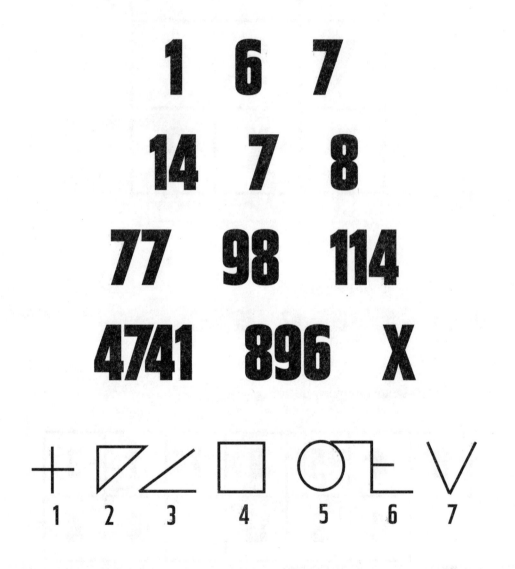

A Magic Word Square

264 Magic Squares can be very intriguing, whether they use number in which each line, column and diagonal adds up to the same number, or whether they use words.
Usually a magic word square consists of a number of different words which can be read both across and down as in the example:

K	I	N	D
I	D	E	A
N	E	A	T
D	A	T	A

However, below is a magic word square with a difference.

Can you fill in the three missing letters so that this is, indeed, a magic word square?

S	I		D
E	I	O	I
R		N	G
P	A		I

265 Which vase is wrong?

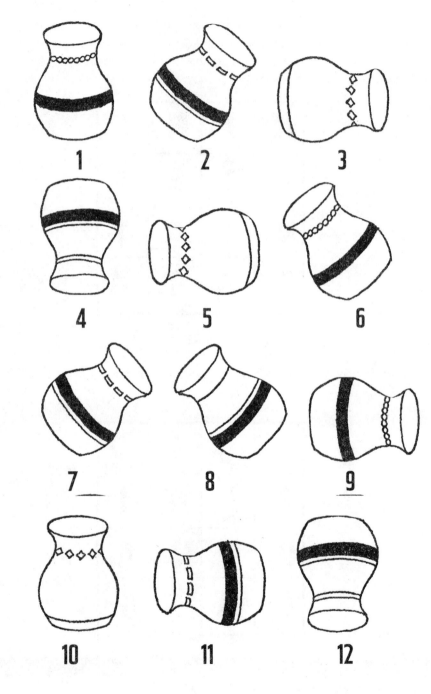

266 Which one is wrong?

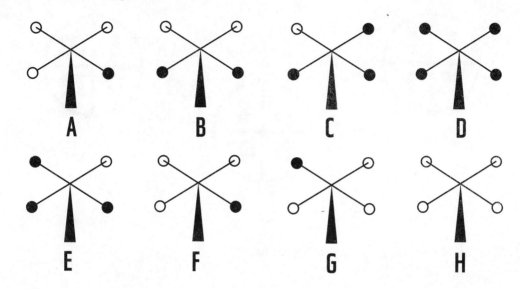

267 What should take the place of X?

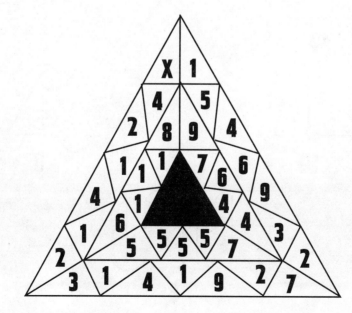

268 What is X?

269 Which pattern does not conform with the others?

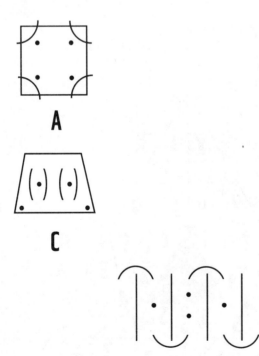

A

B

C

D

E

270 Each of the nine squares in the grid marked 1A to 3C, should incorporate all the lines and symbols which are shown in the squares of the same letter and number immediately above and to the left. For example, 2B should incorporate all the lines and symbols that are in 2 and B.

One of the squares is incorrect. Which one is it?

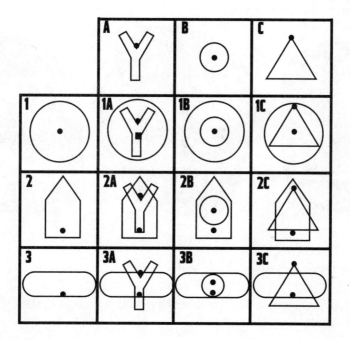

271 Arrange the four strips into a perfect square.

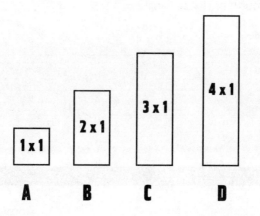

Puzzle 272

Strange Markings

272 Charlie and Bob were demolishing an old house.

When they reached the children's bedroom they found three stones containing very strange markings.

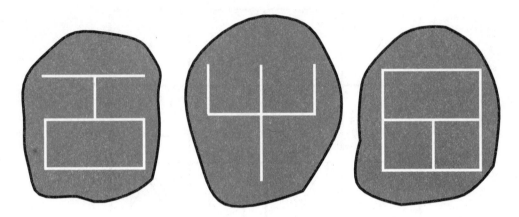

"Must be some sort of hieroglyphics", said Charlie.

"Possibly", said Bob, "but more likely it was one of the children setting a puzzle for one of his brothers or sisters".

"Aha", said Charlie, "and I think I have just solved the puzzle, here's another brick with some more markings, which must be the answer".

What markings did the fourth brick have on it?

273 Which cup is the odd one out?

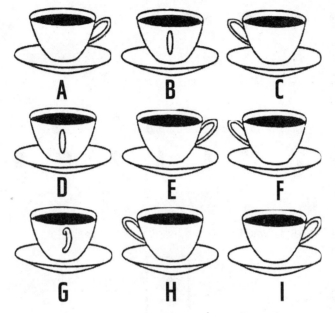

274 What is the total of the spots on the rear side?

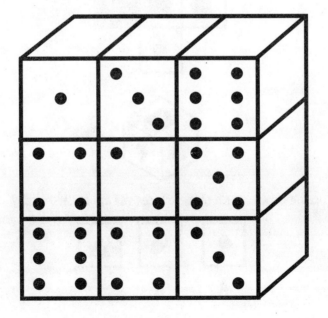

275 What comes next?

124 81 6 32 641 2 –

276 What are A, B, C and D?

3 27 1 32 4 26 3 29

5 25 5 26 6 A B C D

277 If this shape were folded along the dotted lines it could be made into a cube:

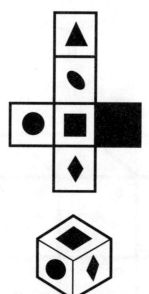

like this:

If this cube is turned upside-down, which of these faces will appear at the top?

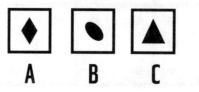

A   B   C

Snooker

278 The game of snooker is played with 15 red balls, a black ball, a pink, a blue, a brown, a green, a yellow, and a white ball, which is the cue ball.

Apart from the reds, which form a triangle at the top of the table, and the white, each of the remaining coloured balls must be placed on its own spot on the table prior to the commencement of a game.

Two novices were setting up their first ever game. They knew where to place the 15 red balls and that the white was the cue ball, and of the remaining seven balls knew where to place the black and pink balls, but hadn't a clue which of the remaining four balls went on which spot, so decided to guess and spot the four balls anywhere.

What were the chances that they would spot all four balls in the correct position?

Also what were the chances they would spot just three of the four balls in the correct position?

279 If this design were turned 90° anti-clockwise and held in front of a mirror, which of the designs below would be reflected?

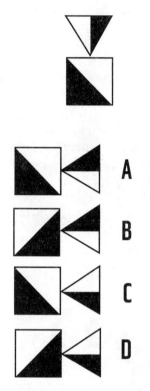

280 What is X?

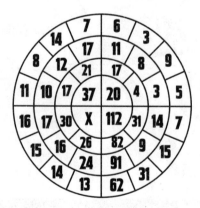

281 What does the third clock show?

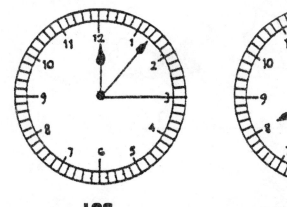

LOG

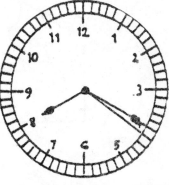

HUT

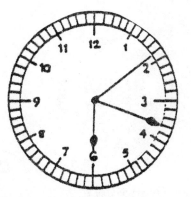

282 Which number is nearest to the number which is midway between the lowest and highest number?

11	84	41	9	79
81	7	36	51	47
88	12	8	89	10

283 Which piece completes the jigsaw puzzle?

A

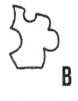

B

C

E

D

F

284 What comes next?

$1^2/_3$ **2.75** **3.8** $4^5/_6$

$5^6/_7$ **6.875** –

The Excited Dog

285 A man is walking his dog on the lead towards home at a steady 4 mph. When they are 10 miles from home the man lets the dog off the lead. The dog immediately runs off towards home at 6 mph. When the dog reaches the house it turns round and runs back to the man at the same speed. When it reaches the man it turns back for the house. This is repeated until the man gets home and lets in the dog. How many miles does the dog cover from being let off the lead to being let in the house?

Puzzle 286

The Early Arrival

286 My wife usually leaves work at 5.30pm, calls at the supermarket, then catches the 6pm train which arrives at our home town station at 6.30pm. I leave home each day, drive to the station and pick up my wife at 6.30pm just as she gets off the train. One day last week my wife was able to finish work about 10 minutes earlier than usual, decided to go straight to the station instead of calling at the supermarket and managed to catch the 5.30pm train which arrived at our home town station at 6pm. Because I was not there to pick her up she began to walk home. I left home at the usual time, saw my wife walking, turned round, picked her up and drove home, arriving there 12 minutes earlier than usual. For how long had my wife walked before I picked her up?

287 A colour is concealed in each of these sentences:

A Temper or anger are signs of weakness.

B The money is for Edward.

C You'll find I got it elsewhere.

D One dancer, I see, is out of step.

E 'I'm a gent and a lady's man,' he said.

288 Here are six clocks turned upside down. Which shows the nearest time to 2.25 if held in front of a mirror? (Don't use a mirror or turn the page.)

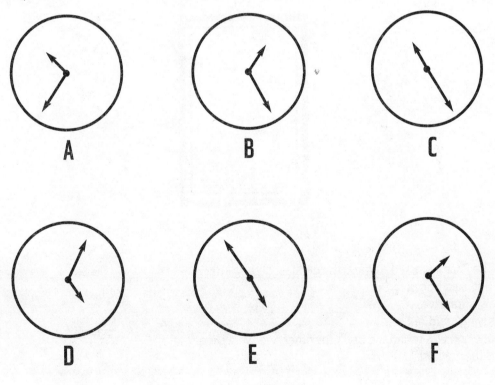

289 Complete the last line:

17	(35)	19
22	(46)	26
31	(65)	37
44	(92)	52
–	(–)	–

290 My mirror is flat. The wall is plumb and the floor horizontal. I can see myself in the mirror from top to toe. I am 5′ 5″ tall. How long is the mirror?

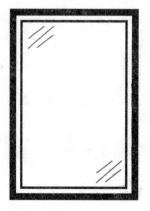

291 The Pharoah asked: "Who is the greatest of the gods?"
'I am not" said Horus.
"Anubis is" said Isis.
"Isis is lying", said Anubis.
Only one god was telling the truth, the other two were lying.
Who is the greatest?

Number Logic

292

	10	7	3
1	4	15	11
8		2	6
16		5	9

Apart from the numbers 12,13 and 14, the numbers 1-16 have been inserted into the grid almost, but not quite, at random.

Following just two simple rules, where would you place the numbers 12,13 and 14 in the grid?

Puzzle 293

Crocodile

293 The crocodile had a tail that was three times as long as its head and its body was half as long as its tail.

Its body and tail measured 171 inches.

How long was its head?

294 Which is the odd one out?

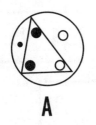

A

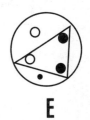

B

C

D

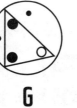

E

F

G

295

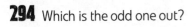

is to

as is to **?**

A

B

C

D

296 What set of numbers comes next?

| 2 | 3 | 4 |

| 9 | 10 | 11 |

| 24 | 25 | 26 |

| 55 | 56 | 57 |

| 118 | 119 | 120 |

| – | – | – |

297 What goes into the empty brackets?

34 (3916) 102

26 (4436) 104

14 ( ) 70

298 Can you discover six male forenames in the outer ring and six female names in the inner ring?

Rat-A-tacks!

299 In the rat-infested village of Cattatackya last month each cat killed the same number of rats as every other cat. The total number of rat fatalities during the month came to 2117.

Less than 50 cats achieved this remarkable feat. How many cats were there in Cattatackya, and how many rats did each kill?

Puzzle 300

300 In the game of snakes and ladders the counter is moved according to the throw of the die. When it lands on the foot of a ladder, it moves to the top of the ladder; when it lands on the head of a snake it moves down to the tail. What will be the total of the numbers reached after the following throws of the die? (Do NOT include the squares at the bottom of the ladders or the tops of the snakes in the total, i.e. the first throw = 15, NOT 20):

5   4   4   2   6   3   2   2

100	99	98	97	96	95	94	93	92	91
81	82	83	84	85	86	87	88	89	90
71	72	73	74	75	76	77	78	79	80
61	62	63	64	65	66	67	68	69	70
51	52	53	54	55	56	57	58	59	60
41	42	43	44	45	46	47	48	49	50
31	32	33	34	35	36	37	38	39	40
21	22	23	24	25	26	27	28	29	30
11	12	13	14	15	16	17	18	19	20
1	2	3	4	5	6	7	8	9	10

301 What is X?

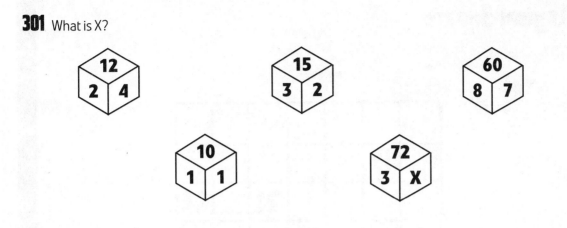

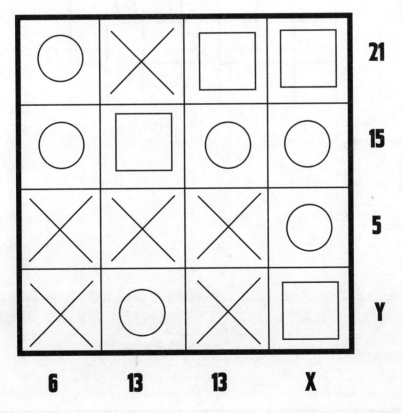

302 Give values for X and Y.

Logical Square

303

	15					
				21		24
?			31			
				12	42	
			11			

What number logically should replace the question mark?

The Mind Boggles

304 A boggle puzzle is where a word or a number can be read by moving from square to square horizontally, vertically or diagonally, as distinct from a conventional word search puzzle, where all the words or numbers are read in a straight line. Examples of each are shown below:

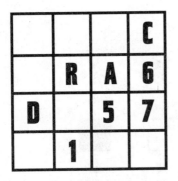

BOGGLE   **WORD SEARCH**

In the puzzle below consecutive years of the 20th-century are written boggle style, starting with the year 1901 and continuing with subsequent years 1902, 1903, 1904 etc. How many consecutive years of the 20th-century can you find before you get to a missing year? You cannot use a square twice for the same year, however, every square may be used as many times as you wish for different years.

3	8	7	6	4
4	3	2	4	9
9	2	9	0	8
0	1	5	1	7
6	3	9	4	1

305 Which of these statements are true and which are false?

A When a car is driven forwards the wheels rotate anti-clockwise.
B If a clock is put forward 1¼ hours the minute hand moves through 450°.
C When a clock reads 4.10 the acute angle between the hands is exactly 60°.

306 Which is the odd one out?

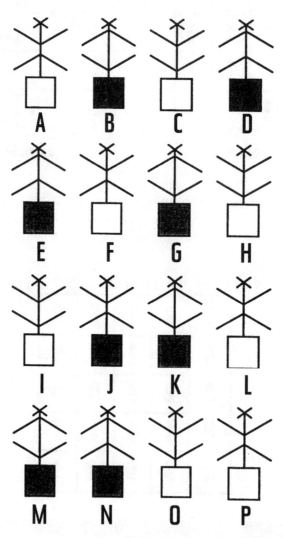

307 What is X?

3	4	6	5
2	15	105	4
7	480	X	8
8	9	6	7

308 What will be the result if the hands of this clock are moved as follows:

A. forward 3 hours, 15 minutes

B. back 4 hours, 25 minutes

C. back 1 hour, 30 minutes

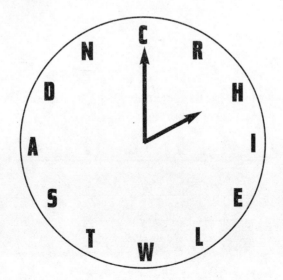

309 Three players each throw three darts that, starting from X, score as follows:

A clockwise: the first three numbers divisible by 3 – all doubles;
B anti-clockwise: the first three numbers divisible by four – all doubles;
C clockwise: the first three numbers divisible by four – all trebles.

What did each player score?

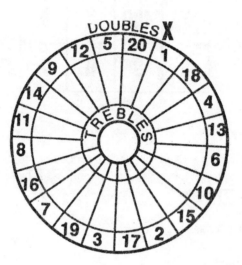

310 Insert arithmetical signs between these numbers to justify the equation. There are two different solutions.

$$1 \quad 2 \quad 3 \quad 4 \quad 5 \quad 6 \quad 7 \quad = \quad 3$$

311 The ball in A moves clockwise, first one letter, then missing one and going onto the next, then missing two, and so on. If it lands on a consonant the ball in B moves to one number clockwise; if it lands on a vowel the ball in B moves to the third number anti-clockwise. If the ball in B lands on an even number the ball in C moves three letters clockwise; if it lands on an odd number the ball in C moves four letters anti-clockwise. What word will be spelt by the ball in C after seven moves?

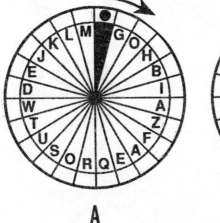

A

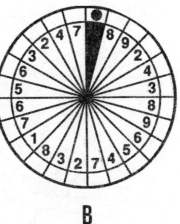

B

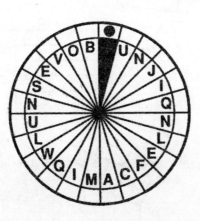

C

312 This wall has been demolished by a careless driver. Can you reconstruct it from four of the pieces below?

Swimming Pool

313 My wife and I were filling the swimming pool with two hosepipes, but unknown to us we were making very little headway as I had left the drainage valve open.

My wife could normally fill the swimming pool with the hosepipe she was using in 9 minutes, however, the hosepipe I was using would normally take 24 minutes, however, the drainage valve would normally empty the pool in 36 minutes.

To the nearest minute, how long would it take us to fill the swimming pool?

Conundrum Chase

314 The following are the runners for the Conundrum Chase at Sandown Park. The form shown is the position finished by each horse in its previous 8 races. Unfortunately the form for the 6th runner has been omitted. Can you work out what its form should be?

3 miles	Conundrum Chase Sandown Park	2.30

Number	Horse	Form
1	Little Snapper	14623256
2	Touchwood	22546316
3	Desert Storm	34126625
4	Water Cress	62245631
5	Summerset	64321562
6	Heathcliffe	?

315 How many different routes are there from A to B?

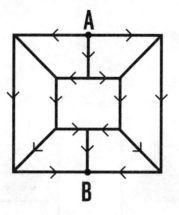

316 Which of the designs below – A, B,C or D – follows number 6?

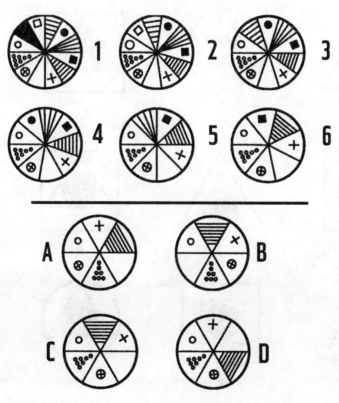

317 Using only plus or minus signs, arrange the numbers below so that they will equal 10. You must use all the numbers.

3   4   5   6   7   8   9

318 Which is the odd one out?

A

B

C

D

E

F

G

H

I

J

K

L

M

N

O

P

319 Choosing from the numbers on the right, what is X?

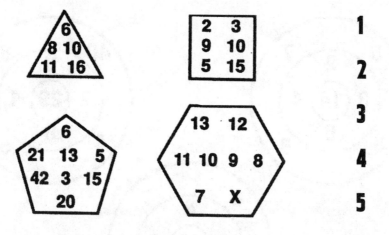

1

2

3

4

5

320 Which of the clocks at the bottom – A, B, C or D – should follow number 5?

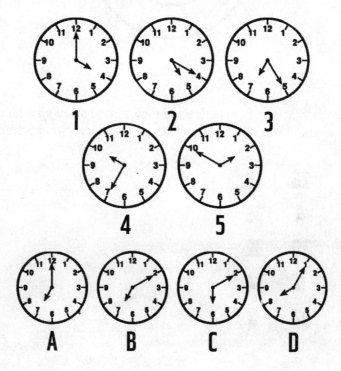

321 What is X?

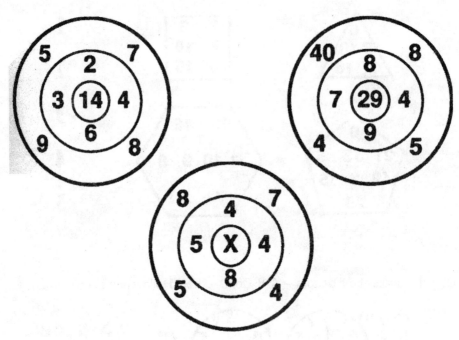

322 Multiply the number that is midway between the lowest and the highest number by the one that is midway between the number that is nearest to the lowest number and the one that is nearest to the highest number.

5	**16**	**28**	**23**
19	**7**	**4**	**38**
21	**15**	**30**	**39**
22	**3**	**6**	**34**
12	**25**	**37**	**8**

323 How many cubes can you count here?

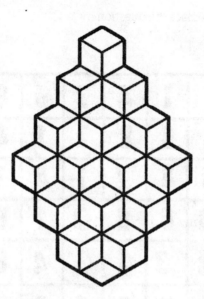

324 Which is the odd one out?

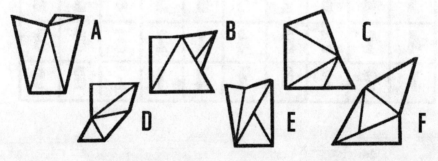

Puzzle 325

G-G-Griddle

325 What numbers should replace the question marks?

6	8	2	1	4	3	6	8	2	1
3	4	3	6	8	2	1	4	3	4
4	1	6	8	2	1	4	3	6	3
1	2	3	6	8	2	1	6	8	6
2	8	4	3	4	3	4	8	2	8
8	6	1	?	?	6	3	2	1	2
6	3	2	?	?	8	6	1	4	1
3	4	8	2	8	6	3	4	3	4
4	1	6	3	4	1	2	8	6	3
1	2	8	6	3	4	1	2	8	6

326 What are X and Y?

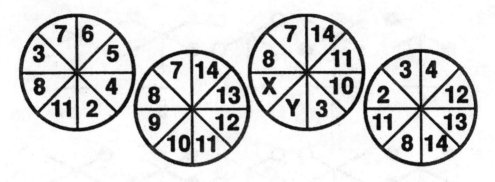

327 Which one is wrong?

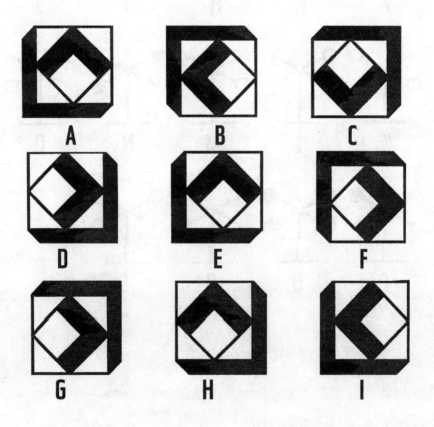

328 Which two make a pair?

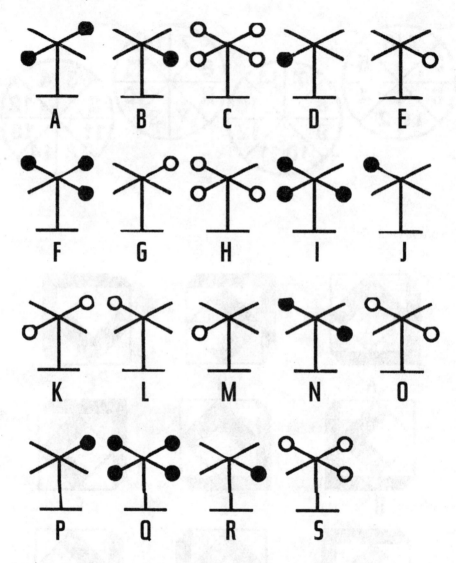

329 What are X, Y and Z?

330 Which of the designs at the bottom should occupy the empty space?

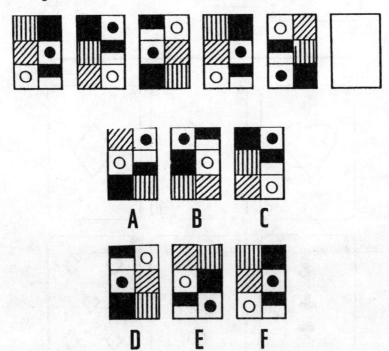

331 What comes next in the series?

625 1296 25   36   5   –

332 Study the top cards and find what city is represented by the bottom cards.

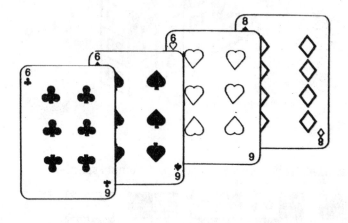

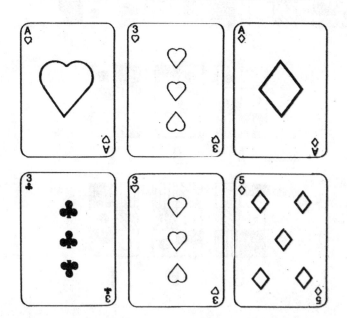

Number Logic

333 Where logically would you place number 1 in the grid?

	9					
				8		
		7				
5					6	
			4			3
					2	

334 What is the last term in the bottom line?

$\frac{1}{5}$	.4	$\frac{3}{5}$	.8	1
$\frac{1}{3}$	1	$1\frac{2}{3}$	2.33	3
$\frac{1}{4}$	1	$1\frac{3}{4}$	2.5	$3\frac{1}{4}$
$\frac{1}{8}$	.625	$1\frac{1}{8}$	1.625	–

335 What is X?

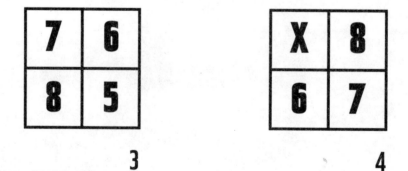

336 What should go into the empty brackets?

305	(6165)	13
280	(5670)	14
145	(2925)	5
70	(1415)	3
25	( )	1

337 Which circle should replace the question mark?

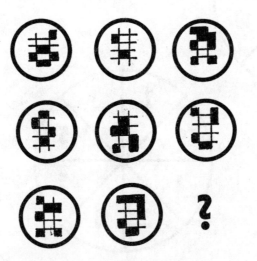

338 Simplify:

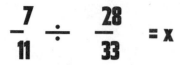

$$\frac{7}{11} \div \frac{28}{33} = x$$

339 Which number should replace the question mark?

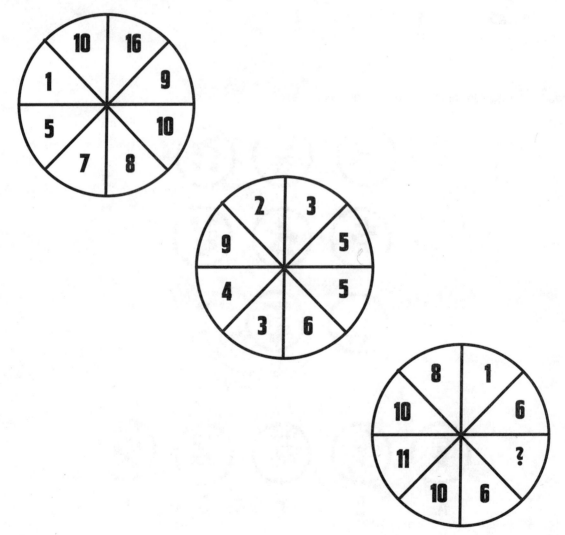

340 Which letter should replace the question mark?

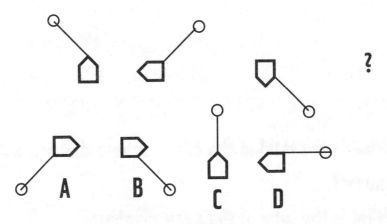

341 Divide the diamond into four equal shapes each containing one of each of the six symbols.

342 If you threw two dice simultaneously, what would be the odds against throwing two sixes?

343 This is an exercise in mental arithmetic, and must be solved without writing anything except the answers,

A What is the total of the odd numbers that are not prime numbers?
B What is the total of the even numbers?
C What is the total of the prime numbers?

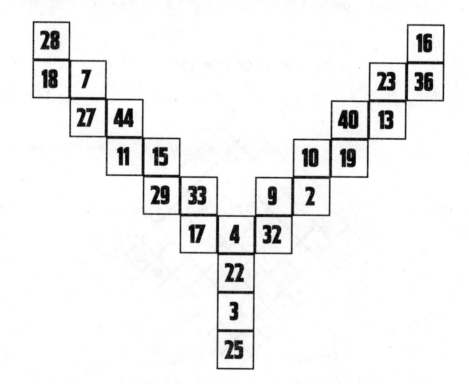

Series

344 Can you draw the next figure in this series?

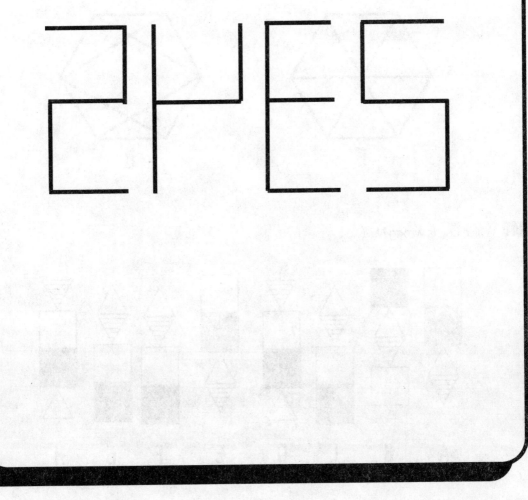

345 What is the total number of triangles in these four hexagons?

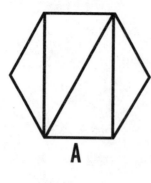

A

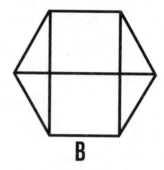

B

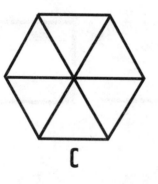

C

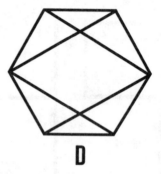

D

346 Which one is wrong?

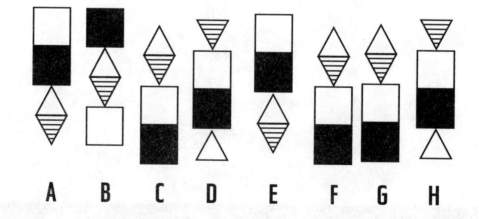

A   B   C   D   E   F   G   H

347 Take two numbers from each circle so that the total of the six numbers chosen is 100.

A

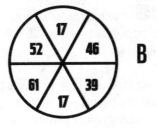

B

C

348 The three circles rotate independently of each other.

Circle A moves one number at a time clockwise;
Circle B moves two places at a time anti clockwise;
Circle C moves three places at a time anti clockwise.

In how many moves will all the eights be together again?

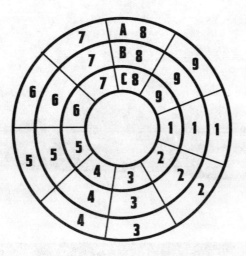

Puzzle 349

The Collectors Bequest

349 A rich collector of gold coins left detailed instructions as to how his gold coin collection of between 300 and 400 coins was to be distributed to his five sons and five daughters after his death.

First of all one gold coin was to be given to his butler, then exactly a fifth of those remaining went to his eldest son. Another coin was then given to his butler, then exactly a fifth of those remaining went to his second eldest son. This procedure was repeated until all his five sons had received a share, and the butler had received 5 gold coins. Then after the fifth son had received his share, the coins still remaining were equally divided between his five daughters.

How many coins were originally in the collection?

350 Which two make a matching pair?

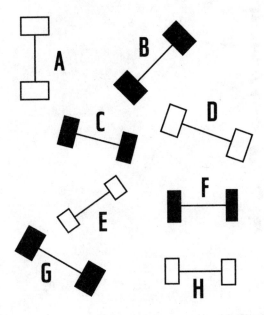

351 Taking one number from each column and using each number only once, how many groups of three that add up to 10 can you find?

1	8	1
6	5	3
9	4	1
3	1	3
5	1	2
2	0	1
4	7	0
7	4	2
0	0	2
8	9	1

352 Which is the odd one out?

A 9 8 6 3 1 4 7

B 6 1 5 3 2 0 3

C 4 7 9 0 1 8 2

D 1 6 7 2 1 0 4

E 3 2 4 4 2 8 6

F 4 6 7 3 1 1 2

G 7 8 8 1 1 9 4

353 What are A, B and C? (There are three clues.)

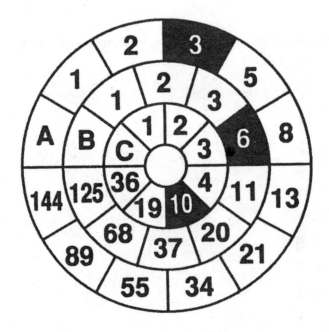

354 If 54 balls are placed into the three receptacles, so that there are twice as many in the cylinder and bucket combined as there are in the box, and twice as many in the box as there are in the bucket, how many balls are there in the cylinder?

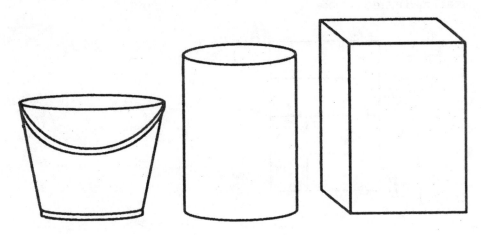

355 This problem is for mental solving only! Do not use a pencil and paper. Add the alternative numbers in A to the alternate numbers in B and divide the result by the sum of the alternate numbers in C.

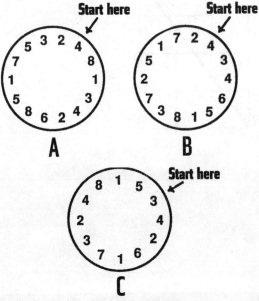

Puzzle 356

Routes

356 How many different routes are there from A to B. Each route must not travel over the same piece of road more than once.

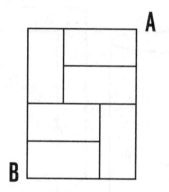

For example, one possible route is shown below.

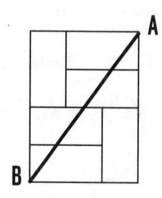

Fifteen Magic

357

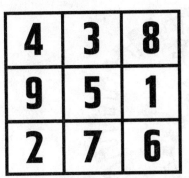

In the above each horizontal, vertical and corner to corner line totals 15. But what if the number 8 is repositioned as below? Is it still possible to place a different number in each square so that each horizontal, vertical and corner to corner line again totals 15? You will find, that with a bit of lateral thinking, it is possible.

358 In these epicyclic gears, when pinion A completes three revolutions where will the tooth marked X on pinion B be? Choose from A, B, C and D below.

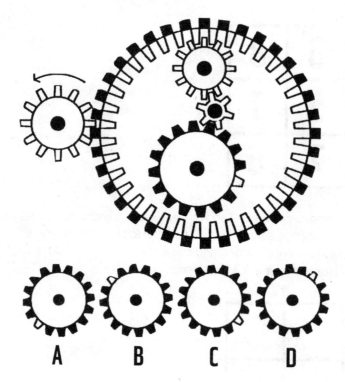

A   **B**   **C**   **D**

359 Three receptacles contain certain amounts of water as indicated below. How much water would have to be poured from A into B and C so that each receptacle contains the same?

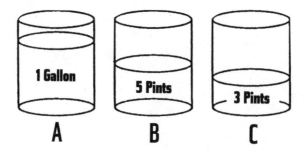

1 Gallon   5 Pints   3 Pints

A   **B**   **C**

360 Which is the odd one out?

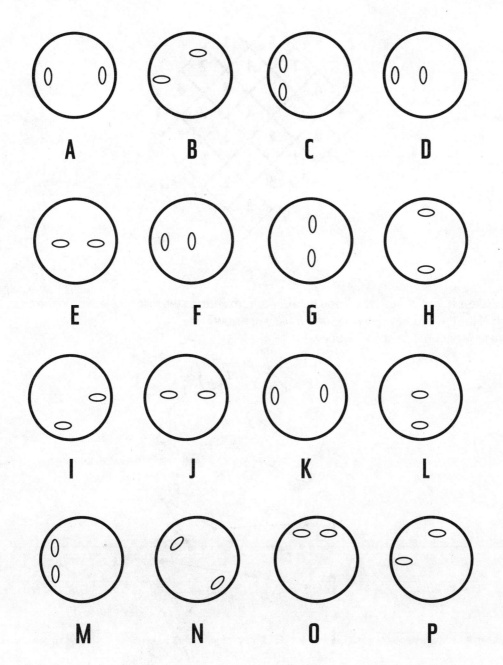

361 What are X, Y and Z?

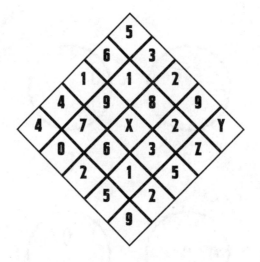

362 Here is a map of Australia. If you flew direct from Perth to the following towns in the order listed, which of the three routes shown below would you follow?

Adelaide Melbourne Brisbane Sydney

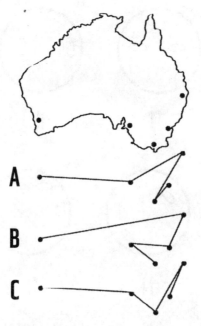

Sequence

363   3

       13

       1113

       3113

       2123

       112213

       312213

       212223

       114213

       ?

What comes next?

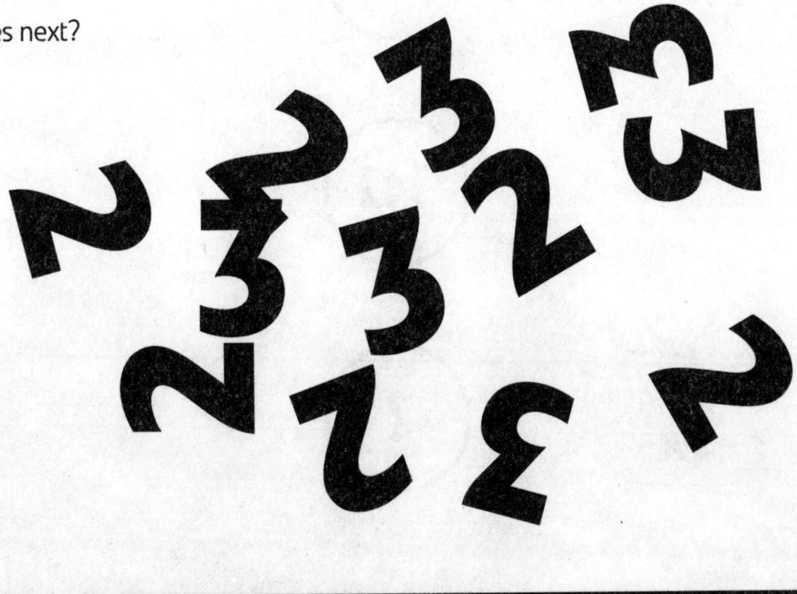

Puzzle 364

Dials

364 What number is missing from the bottom dial?

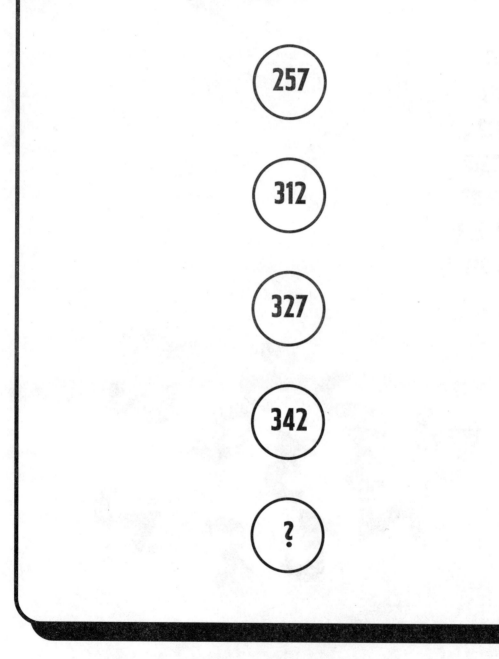

365 What is X?

3 12 83 130 3 130 313 1303 1 X 31

366 What is X?

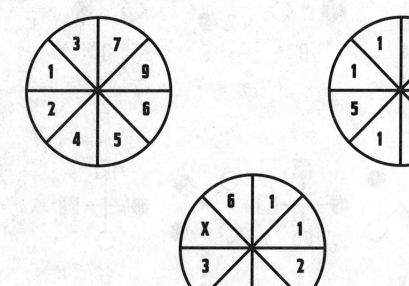

367 Multiply the number that is midway between the lowest number and the one that is nearest to the highest number by the number that is midway between the highestnumber and the one that is nearest to the lowest number.

39 9 26 49 5
35 51 43 14 41
8 11 7 38 30

368 Which is the odd one out?

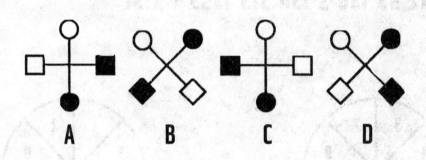

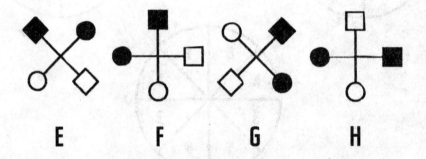

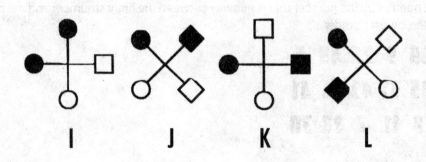

369 Which five of the pieces shown below will form the square?

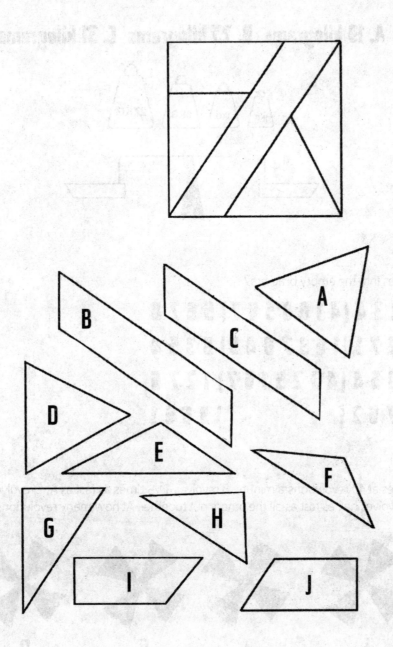

370 How would you arrange the weights on the pans of the scales so that you could weigh the following?

A. 19 kilograms B. 25 kilograms C. 31 kilograms

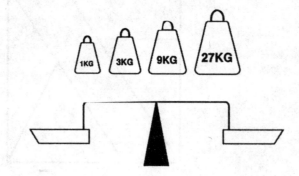

371 What goes into the empty brackets?

1 2 3 4 (4 1 6 3 5 8 7) 5 6 7 8

6 2 7 1 (1 6 3 7 8 4 5) 8 3 5 4

3 8 5 4 (4 3 2 5 1 6 7) 1 2 7 6

4 7 6 2 (   ) 3 6 5 1

372 A revolves at 40 revolutions a minute; B revolves $1\frac{1}{2}$ times as fast as A; C revolves twice as fast as B; and D revolves half as fast as all the others put together. At how many revolutions a minute does D revolve?

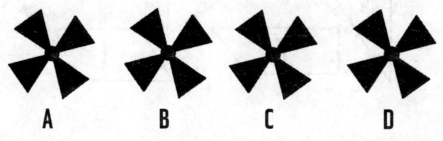

A   B   C   D

373 Each of the nine squares in the grid marked 1A to 3C, should incorporate all the lines and symbols which are shown in the squares of the same letter and number immediately above and to the left.

For example, 2B should incorporate all the lines and symbols that are in 2 and B. One of the squares is incorrect. Which one is it?

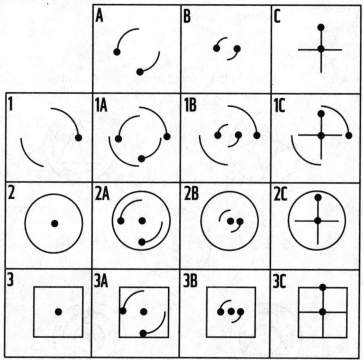

374 These 12 objects can be placed in 3 sets of 4. The sets are:
4 DOGS, 4 ANIMALS, 4 REPTILES

CLUMBER	BONGO	TUMBLER	ROEBUCK
POINTER	LURCHER	AGUTI	TAIPAN
TERRIER	CAIMAN	SAURIAN	PADDOCK

375 Each line and symbol which appears in the four outer circles, in the top diagram, is transferred to the centre circle according to these rules:

If a line or symbol occurs in the outer circles:
once: it is transferred
twice: it is possibly transferred
3 times: it is transferred
4 times: it is not transferred.

Which of the circles A, B, C, D, E, shown below should appear at the centre of the top diagram?

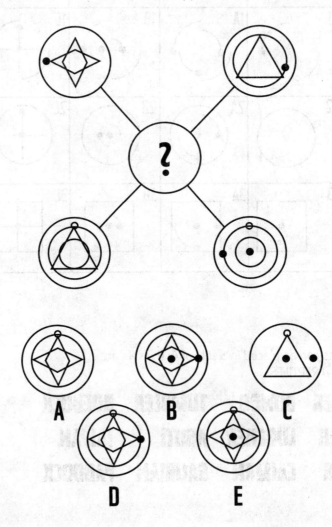

Missing Number

376 "Here's a puzzle for you", said young Tony to his classmate. "What is the missing number in this sequence?"

7, ? , 951, 620, 3

"Not sure" replied Susan, "will I need a calculator to work it out?" "A calculator might help" replied Tony.

"Aha!, I see what you mean" said Sue.

What is the missing number?

Puzzle 377

Apples

377 My neighbour returned from his orchard with an armful of apples. To my youngest son he gave half of the apples plus half an apple. To my second eldest son he gave half what he had left plus half an apple and to my eldest son he also gave half what he had left plus half an apple.

He then had no apples left.

How many apples did he have originally?

378 Which of the numbered arrows belongs to X?

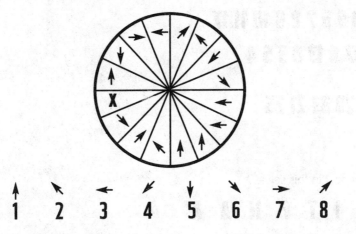

379 Pinion A is the driving pinion, while pinion B idles on its stub axle.
The black teeth of these pinions are in mesh with teeth in the outer ring.
(A) After four revolutions of A in an anti-clockwise direction, where will the black tooth of pinion B be?
(B) And where will it be when A has revolved clockwise through one revolution and then to where the tooth marked X meshes with the outer ring?

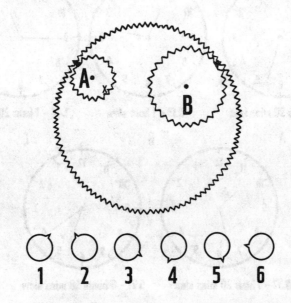

380 Which of the numbers in the bottom line should be placed under 17 in the top line?

2 3 4 5 6 7 8 9 10 11 17

7 2 17 6 13 8 3 5 4

9 15 20 33 21 25

381 What comes next in this series?

I S I T P N A A

D L I I Y N –

382 These clocks are all wrong, as indicated. If they are all correctly adjusted, which clock will show the nearest time to 12 o'clock?

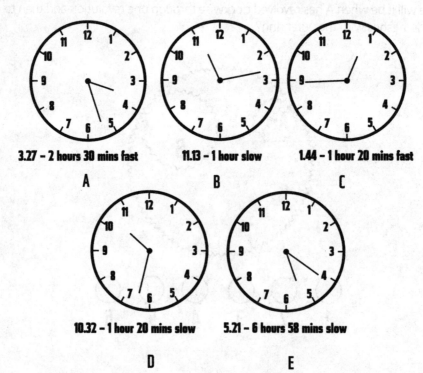

3.27 – 2 hours 30 mins fast
A

11.13 – 1 hour slow
B

1.44 – 1 hour 20 mins fast
C

10.32 – 1 hour 20 mins slow
D

5.21 – 6 hours 58 mins slow
E

383 Imagine that blocks X and Y are removed from the arrangement below, and that the remaining shape is turned upside-down. Which of the other shapes will be the result?

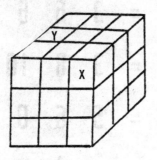

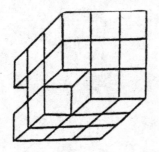

A

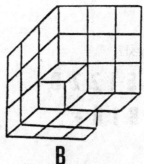

B

C

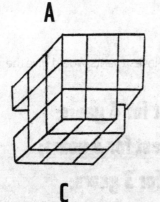

D

384

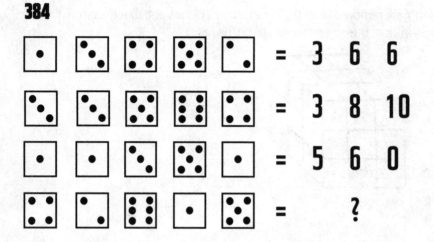

= 3 6 6

= 3 8 10

= 5 6 0

= ?

385 What comes next?

2 3 4 6 1 2 2 0
1 8 4 8 1 0 -

386 Without using a pocket calculator, which of these investments would give the greatest interest?

A £1,000 @ 5% simple interest for 4 years;

B £700 @ 8% compound interest for 3 years;

C £900 @ 7% simple interest for 3 years;

D £800 @ 6% compound interest for 4 years.

What's The Number?

387 "What number is missing from this sequence?" asked Sally

4, 6, 2, 7, ?, 4, 8

"I think it should be 4 " replied Hilary.

"So, what comes next in this sequence?" asked Hilary

2, 4, 5, 4, 2, 4, ?

"I know it is 8 ", said Sally

"Correct" said Hilary.

"This is all beyond me", said John, "but try me with another."

"OK" said Sally, "What number comes between four and four in the sequence below?"

4, 6, 5, 7, 4 ,?, 4, 2, 3, 8, 5

Can you solve the puzzle?

Clocks

388 The five clocks on adjoining platforms at our local train station seem to have developed a mind of their own.

The clocks on platforms 1 - 4 are shown below.

What should be the time of the clock on platform 5?

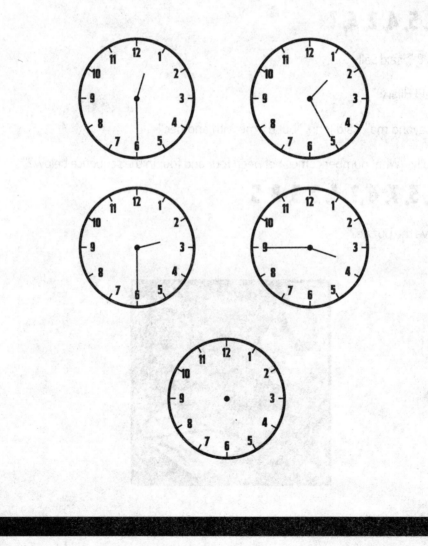

389 Which of these statements are true and which are false?

(A) 1 mile in 55 seconds shows a higher average speed that $\frac{3}{4}$ mile in 50 seconds.

(B) 2 gallons is more than 9 litres.

(C) The area of this rectangle

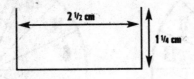

is greater than the area of this circle

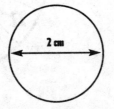

(D) Given that a jack counts as 11 and queen as 12 and a king as 13, the total number of spots on a set of dominoes is greater than that of all the picture cards.

390 What is X?

3	4	5	9	6	7	8
12	10	9	10	11	16	14
7	3	2	30	12	13	17
1	2	3	24	9	10	11
41	7	8	X	22	19	16

391 What is X?

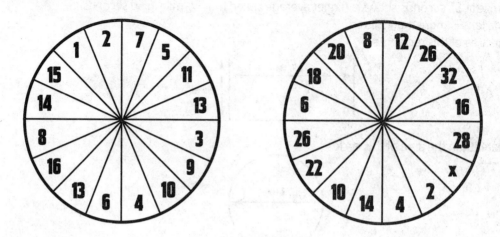

392 What comes next in this series?

1 2 6 2 4 1 2 0 7 2 0 5 0 4   –

393 Each day the hour hand moves forward one hour, while the minute hand goes back five minutes. In how many days will the clock show eleven o'clock?

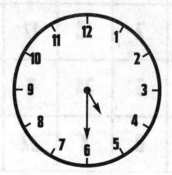

394 In the game of 'running out' at dominoes each player has to lay a domino so that the number of spots on one half matches those exposed at either end of the previously laid dominoes, as follows:

If the next player held the domino shown below it could be placed at either end, with the 1-spot matching that on the left or the 4-spot matching that in the right:

In the layout of a game shown below the order in which the dominoes were played is indicated. Can you detect the two fallacies in this? (Indicate by the numbers printed beside the dominoes.)

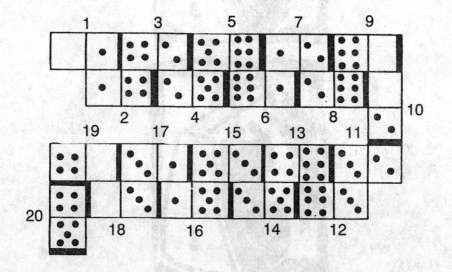

Probability

395 Two identical bags each contain eight balls, four white and four black.

One ball is drawn out of bag one and another ball out of bag two.

What are the chances that at least one of the balls will be black?

396 What are X, Y, and Z?

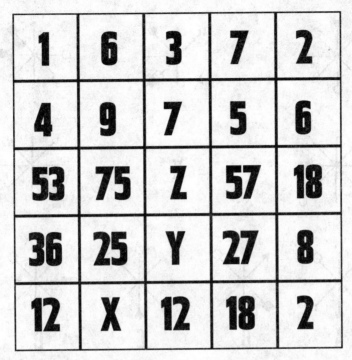

1	6	3	7	2
4	9	7	5	6
53	75	Z	57	18
36	25	Y	27	8
12	X	12	18	2

397 Five towns, A, B, C, D and E, are situated consecutively so that when joined by straight roads they form the five points of an irregular pentagon.

B is 100 miles from A, its right-hand neighbour; E is 50 miles from D, its right-hand neighbour. From A to C via B is 125 miles; E is 75 miles from its neighbour, A, and 70 miles from C.

1 What is the length of the journey from A to E via B, C and D?

2 How far from B is E by the shortest route?

3 What is the distance from C to D?

398 Which of the figures below belongs to X?

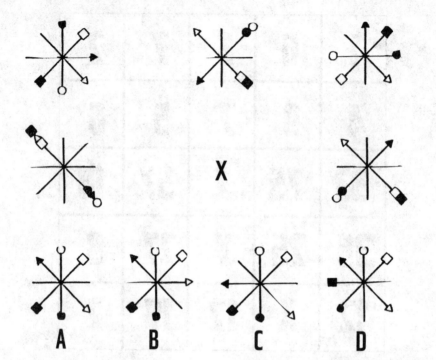

399 What is X?

2	3	12	1
4	1	5	12
9	4	17	80
6	5	24	37
3	8	32	41
5	2	11	18
7	3	X	28

400 In a cricket match, each player of one team was bowled 1st ball. Which player was 0 not out?

401

is to

as

is to

A   B   C   D   E

Puzzle 402

Time Teaser

402 Three trains start at different times on a 100-mile journey. Train A leaves 10 minutes late and stops at a station for 5 minutes. Its average speed is 40mph. Train B leaves 20 minutes late and stops at a station for 14 minutes. Its average speed is 50mph. Which train completes the journey in the shortest time?

403 These 12 creatures can be placed in 3 sets of 4. The 3 sets are:
4 ANIMALS, 4 FISH, 4 BIRDS

DOTTREL	**SQUID**	**LAMPREY**	**BUBALIS**
DASYPUS	**BITTERN**	**BANTING**	**CHAFFINCH**
MERLING	**HAMSTER**	**GROUPER**	**DOVE**

404 What number should replace the ?

121	100	?	64	49

405 What time should appear on the 4th clock?

406 This clock has gone mad! Every minute the second hand goes back - first one second, then two, then three and so on; the minute hand goes forward first two minutes, then three, then four and so on; the hour hand goes back first three hours, then four, then five and so on. What exact time will it show five minutes from now?

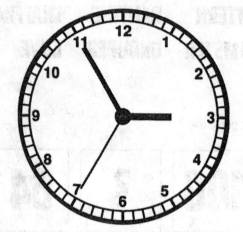

407 What is X?

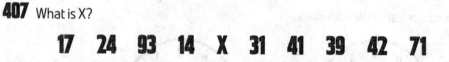

17   24   93   14   X   31   41   39   42   71

408 How many minutes before 12 noon is it if 50 minutes ago it was four times as many minutes past 10?

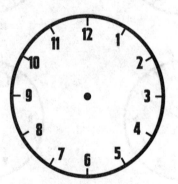

409 6 3 7 4 is to G F D C

as

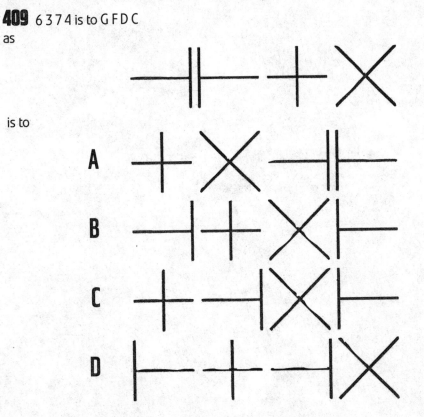

is to

A

B

C

D

410 Which is the granny knot among the reef knots?

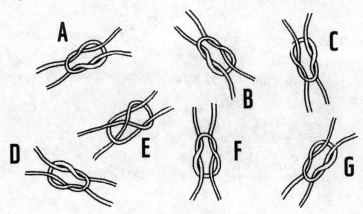

Answers

1 D
The bottom figure is below the higher figure.

2 A is 9, B is 11, C is 8, D is 12
If the four corners are numbered:

1	2
3	4

the numbers in the four corners of the second overall square in each pair are as follows:

1+4	2+3
1+3	2+4

3 ANN
give each letter a number according to its position in the alphabet.
TED = 20 + 5 + 4 (29)
ANN = 1 + 14 + 14 (29)
(George and Mary each add to 57)

4 E
The knob is on the wrong side.

5 C
VIII has taken place of VII.

6 40

7 E
The design consists of the letter S repeated 10 times, but in E one of them is the wrong way round.

Answers 8-13

8 105

9 25

10 5 men, 10 children and 20 women

If x = the number of men, then $x + 2x + 4x = 35$

therefore $7x = 35$

so $x = 5$

11 A-C, B-F, D-G, E-H

12

	EVEN	ODD	PRIME	SQUARE	2 DIGITS	6-12
1		✔		✔		
2	✔		✔			
3		✔	✔			
4	✔			✔		
5		✔	✔			
6	✔					✔
7		✔	✔			✔
8	✔					✔
9		✔		✔		✔
10	✔				✔	✔
11		✔	✔		✔	✔
12	✔				✔	✔
13		✔	✔		✔	
14	✔				✔	
15		✔			✔	
16	✔			✔	✔	

1 is not a prime number

Square numbers are 1, 4, 9, 16

Only 4 ticks means 4 truths

So, 11 is the winner

13 ZERO

He had 3 white socks and 1 black sock in his drawer.

His chances were

Pr white socks	Mixed Pair	Pr Black socks
$\frac{1}{2}$	$\frac{1}{2}$	ZERO

14 A is 9 or 6, B is 6 or 9, C is 6, D is 12
$(9 \times 6 + 6) \div 12 = 5$

15 A is true; B is false (the majority are concave); C is false (a spider has eight legs); D is false (a stalagmite grows upwards, whereas as stalactite grows downwards).

16

OBSERVANCE	of	HERMITS
MELODY	of	HARPERS
EXALTATION	of	LARKS
SIEGE	of	CRANES
WATCH	of	NIGHTINGALES
PARLIAMENT	of	OWLS
COLONY	of	RABBITS
TRIP	of	SHEEP
HUSK	of	HARES
TRIBE	of	GOATS
KENNEL	of	RACHES
CRY	of	HOUNDS

17 1 6 2 7 8 4
The numbers putside the brackets are transposed inside the brackets in the same order as in the top line.

18 52
The results are increased by one and decreased by one alternately:
$17 \times 3 = 51 + 1 = 52$

19 21
There are 15 small hexagons and 6 large ones. The last shape in the bottom row is a pentagon.

20 B
The figure is rotating clockwise.

21 C
The figures are transposed in the same way as in the example at the top.

22 He tilted the butt until the water came up to the top edge without any running over. As the level of the water did not reach point X the butt was not half-full. If it had reached point X, it would have been exactly half full.

But if point X had been submerged it would have been more than half full.

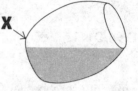

23 5 6 2 5

The first number inside the brackets is the square root of the number outside the brackets. The remaining number inside the brackets is the square of the number outside the brackets.

24 N

There are two black balls instead of one white and one black.

25 Three sisters and two brothers

This can be solved by simple deduction, but if algebra is used let x be the number of sisters and y the number of brothers:

$$x + 1 = 2y$$
$$y + 1 = x$$

Therefore, $y + 1 + 1 = 2y$

so $y = 2$

or $x + 1 = 2x - 2$

so $x = 3$

26 3 – C

Line 1 finishes at 2, and line 2 finishes at 1.

27 59

The first 56 balls could be of all colours *except* red. This would leave 8 balls, all of which are red, so any three chosen would be red.

28 A - F, B - C. D - G and E - H

29 53

37 is midway between 3 (the lowest number) and 71 (the highest number); 53 is midway between 37 and 69 (nearest to the highest number).

30 17 is the smallest segment; 14 is the largest segment.

31 K, which is longer.

32

100.00	Won by	Money in Wallet
1st Hole	A	150.00
2nd	A	225.00
3rd	Tie	225.00
4th	B	112.50
5th	B	56.25
6th	B	28.12
7th	A	42.18
8th	A	63.27
9th	Tie	63.27
10th	A	94.90
11th	A	142.35
12th	B	71.18

It is good way to wager if the 2 players are equal standard, B will always win money if he ties or loses by a few holes, but if A wins by a large number of holes, he will win a fortune.

B, if he won every hole, could only win £100, but A could win a fortune.

33 10

$$
\begin{array}{r}
70 \\
75 \\
85 \\
+ \ 80 \\
\hline
310 \div 3 = 100 \text{ remainder } 10
\end{array}
$$

3 subjects each student, 10 at least 4

34 6+10+13, 8+9+12, 5+6+18, 4+12+13, 8+10+11, 19+4+6, 11+6+12

35 D
B is too big, A and C are too small.

36 B

37 42
There are 5 diamonds made with 9 squares, 12 diamonds made with 4 squares, and 25 diamonds made with 1 square.

Answers 38-47

38 Glass sign on glass door
PULL on one side
PUSH on opposite side

39 Start the 7 and 11 min. hour glasses when the egg is dropped into the water when it is boiling. When the sand stops running in the 7 glass, turn it over. When the sand stops running in the 11 glass, turn the 7 glass again. When the sand stops again in the 7 glass, 15 mins. will have elapsed.

40 1.2cm
The measurement is reduced by $\frac{1}{13}$ (four cards removed from 52).

41 A–D, B–L, C–H, E–G, F–J and I–K

42 I is the second smallest. F is the second largest.

43 0–0 and 5–2

44

TANK	VEHICLE	TRACTOR
CASTLE	TURRET	TANK
BANK	SAND	CASTLE
RIVER	RIPARIAN	BANK
BRIDGE	SEVERN	RIVER
CARDS	YARBOROUGH	BRIDGE
WOOD	JACK	CARDS
BOW	YEW	WOOD
BULLS-EYE	ARROW	BOW
TRACTOR	FARM	BULLS-EYE
SOLUTION 1	SOLUTION 2	

45 C
C results in 4; all the others result in 5.

46 A and F

47 26
Starting at the top left-hand corner and taking every fourth number, there are four series:
1, 2, 3, 4, 5, 6 (bottom left-hand square in centre section), 7, 8, 9; 2, 3, 4, 5, 6, 7 (bottom right-hand square in centre section), 8, 9, 10; 9, 8, 7, 6 (top left-hand square in centre section), 5, 4, 3, 2, 1; and 1, 3, 5, 7 (top right-hand square in centre section), 9, 11, 13, 15, 17.

48 P

It is the only arrow pointing to the left.

49 1020

Multiply the first two numbers in the right-hand column and place the result in the left-hand column; multiply the last two numbers in the right-hand column and place the result in the left-hand column.

50 A

51 A

52   OLIVE, SANDY, ISABEL (colours)

MARTIN, ROBIN, MAVIS (birds)

PRIMROSE, POPPY, MYRTLE (flowers)

GARNET, DIAMOND, PEARL (gems)

53 20

X, C and M are the Roman numerals 10, 100 and 1000 respectively. 1000 divided by 100 is 10; 100 divided by 10 is also 10.

54 E

There are only 7 off-shoots from the centre, instead of 8, as in all the others.

55 147

Add the first two numbers and place the total on the left inside the brackets, then place the difference between the other two numbers on the right inside the brackets.

56 A–C–H, B–E–L, D–G–M and F–I–J; K is the odd one out.

57 5

The numbers represent the alphabetic position of the letters; 1 is A, 4 is D etc. the word becomes ADUMBRATE with the addition of the final E. (One meaning of this word is 'to indicate faintly'.)

58 I

This man has no hands, as seen on his counterpart – E and M.

59 C and E

C goes on the right side of the piece already hung; E goes on the left side.

60 CLEFT

Turn the keys upside down and read the word formed by the lock ends.

61 E and H

In both cases the minute and the hour hands have changed places.

62 1 and 7 are clefs– the G, or treble, clef, and the F, or bass, clef (indicating musical pitch). 3 and 9 are crotchets; 4 and 11 are minims; 5 and 10 are quavers; 6 and 8 are semi-quavers (all musical notes). 2 is a musical time signature, in this case indicating 'common' or 4/4 time. A sit has no counterpart, it is the odd one out.

63 F

There are 5 related pairs:

A (cricket bat) with J (cricket ball)
B (tennis ball) with E (tennis racquet)
C (table tennis bat) with H (table tennis ball)
D (billiards ball) with K (billiards cue)
G (golf ball) with I (golf club)
F (football) is on its own

64 20

The black stripe is too narrow.

65 £61

66 Their ages equalled 72

These are the possible ages:

72 – 1 – 1	The door number	74
36 – 2 – 1		39
24 – 3 – 1		28
18 – 4 – 1		23
18 – 2 – 2		22
12 – 6 – 1		19
12 – 3 – 2		17
9 – 4 – 2		15
8 – 9 – 1		18
8 – 3 – 3		14

6 – 6 – 2	14
6 – 4 – 3	13

The census taker did not know their ages because there were 2 totals of 14.
The door number was 14, so the total was 14

8 – 3 – 3	)	There was an oldest girl
6 – 6 – 2	)	

so it must have been 8 – 3 – 3

67 5040
Multiply each number by 2, 3, 4, 5 and 6 and (finally) 7.

68 X is 193; Y is 63
In the outer ring, starting with the lowest number, each number is doubled and 1 subtracted from the result. In the inner ring, starting with the lowest number, each number is doubled and 1 added to the result. (Alternatively, in the outer ring, the progression is 3, 6, 12, 24, 48 and 96; in the inner ring the progression is 2, 4, 8, 16, 32).

69 A is 4; B is 20; C is 5; D is 2
Add the numbers from top to bottom diagonally to the left of the bottom line for the first three positions on the bottom line, and to the right for the next three positions.

70 A is 2; B is 11; C is 5
The bottom line totals 19; the next line up totals 18; then 17. Hence 16, 15 and 14.

71 D
Examination of the previous globes shows that the globe is rotating left to right.

72 4

73 29
The odd numbers in A total 39; the even numbers in B total 40. From this combined total of 79 is subtracted 50 – the total of the prime numbers in C.

74 X is 2; Y is 8

75 B
The mast is too far forward.

76 A
When the diagonal line from the base-line of the square inclines to the right, as in C, E and G, the right half of the square is black.
When it inclines to the left as in B, D and F, the bottom half of the square is black.
In A the right half of the square should be black.

77 If at first you don't succeed, try, try, again, then quit. There's no sense being a damn fool about it.

78 C
The digits add up to 19. In all the others the total is 18.

79 J
The mouth should be as in B and H.

80 1416
In the first example, divide the left-hand number by 4 and the right-hand number by 5.
In the second example, divide the left-hand number by 6 and the right-hand number by 7. Therefore, in the third line, divide the left-hand number by 8 (14) and the right-hand number by 9 (16).

81 B and M

82 AE, BD, CG, FH

83 18
All the others are divisible by 4

84 F and H

85 X is 6; Y is 1
Starting at number 1 and moving to alternate segments clockwise:
1 2 3 4 5 6
Starting at number 6 and moving in the same way:
6 5 4 3 2 1

86 B

87 E
Adding up each column:
Column A = 75
Column B = 80

Column C = 85
Column D = 90
Column E = 96
Column F = 100

88 Suspension bridge

89 3020
The first 2 digits on the right of the brackets are divided by the digit on the left to gve the first digit inside the brackets. The remaining number on the right of the brackets is multiplied by the digit on the left of the brackets to give the remaining number inside the brackets.

90 A
In each row the first symbol is the same as the second in the previous row and the other symbols continue in the same order.

91 2
The first column totals 9. The second column totals 10. This pattern continues, so the final column should total 13, by the addition of 2.

92 AG CI, BF, DK, EJ, HL

93 G and H

94 X is 4; Y is 11
Two alternate series
Starting with the first number: 7 6 5 4 3
Starting with the second number: 8 9 10 11 12

95
E – tetragon (4 sides)
C – pentagon (5 sides)
B – hexagon (6 sides)
G – heptagon (7 sides)
A – octagon (8 sides)
F – nonagon (9 sides)
D – decagon (10 sides)

96 2 When the head of the match points to the left, that match should lie on top of the other match. In 2 it lies underneath.

97

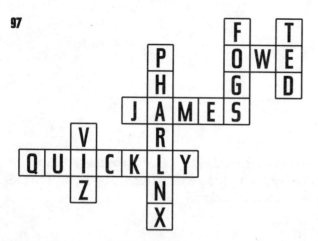

98 No player could have achieved a five digit total. There are no four digit prime palindromic numbers. There are only 15 three digit prime numbers which are palindromic, and one two digit prime palindromic number 11. The total is 7104 divided by 16 equals an average of 444.

99 C
Each row contains one envelope with an upright stamp, one with the stamp sloping to the right and one to the left. The upright stamp (the missing one in the second row) should be cancelled with wavy lines to correspond with the first envelope in the top row, and C is the only one which so conforms.

100 55 squares and 30 triangles

101 1.
From 2 onwards the figure is rotated clockwise, 45 degrees at a time. In each movement the spot alternates from white to black, the heavy and light-shaded portions being alternately transposed in their positions. Number 1 should be as follows:

102
A $x = 9$. The figure in the third square across is the sum of the figures in the preceding two squares.
B $x = 14$. In the first row across the numbers increase by 3 and 4; in the second row by 4 and 5. Therefore, in the third row they should increase by 5 and 6.
C $x = I$. This is similar to the previous example, except that letters are used instead of numbers. In the first row the letters advance, skipping 3 and 4 places respectively. In the second row they should advance, skipping 4 and 5 places, so as to conform with the third row, in which the letters skip 5 and 6 places.

103 85

In the first row, the numbers outside the brackets are divided by 16 and the results placed inside the brackets. In the second row they are divided by 17. Therefore, in the third row they are divided by 18.

104 2, 3, 12 – These losing numbers have been decided by the gambling authorities and apply world wide.

105 AF, BG, CE, DH

106 They are both the same distance from Sheffield *when they meet* !

107 S19

There are two separate series. The letters advance missing first two (A to D), then three (D to H) and so on. After M there must be five missing letters, bringing us to S. The numbers advance in the same way.

108 C

The middle scrolls do not conform with the others.

109 F

Both scrolls are turned the same way; in all the others one is turned inwards and the other outwards.

110 D

As 1764 was a leap year, there were 29 days in February, so it would be Saturday 10 NOT 11 March.

111
1   5.5 KG
2   6.5 KG
3   7 KG
4   4.5 KG
5   3.5 KG

112 C

The cross in the bottom right quarter is different from those in the other shields

113 6

114 112

115 3

The numbers following the letters correspond with the position in the alphabet of the letters.

116 16
4 is the square of 2; 9 is the square of 3; 25 is the square of 5; x must be the square of 4 (16).

117 B
The face in B is composed of three circles, four straight lines and five curves. All the other faces have four circles, four straight lines and four curves.

118 448

119 13
Change the Roman numerals into modern numbers:
208 104 52 26
Each one is half the previous number. therefore the next number is 13, expressed in modern numerals to conform with the established pattern.

120 E
In all the others identical shapes overlap:
A two circles
B two equilateral triangles
C two ovals
D two right-angled triangles
F two squares
In E there are two diamonds which do not overlap

121 D

122 C, D, E

123 CONSTANTINE

124 The figure is turned 45 degrees clockwise each time the black shaded portion moves first from top to bottom (in the first row) and then from left to right (in the second row).

125 E, which has an even number of rungs. All the others have an odd number.

126 A

127 A:12 (Each number doubles its opposite lower number and adds two.)
B: 25 (Each number doubles its opposite lower number and adds three.)

128 Examination of the four correct houses gives the following information:

A The front door is on the same side as the chimney.
B If the front door is on the left, the lower window is a bay window if there is no porch over the door.
C Also, if the front door is on the left, there is a black window over the door if there is no porch and a white window if there is a porch.
D If the front door is on the right, again there is a bay window if there is no porch over the door and a rectangular window if there is.
E If the front door is on the right, however, the window over the door is reversed from previously, that is, if there is no porch there is a white window over the door and if there is a porch there is a black window.

Comparing the four numbered houses with this information we find:
i) House number 1 is correct (front door on left, black window over door and lower bay window).
ii) House number 2 is incorrect because the window over the porch should be black and that over the lower window should be white.
iii) House number 3 is incorrect becasue not only is there a bay window in addition to a porch, but the upper windows are also wrong.
iv) House number 4 is correct and conforms with house B.
Therefore, 2 and 3 are incorrect.

129 A = 7
B = 8
From the music shown the following can be deduced:

after		comes	
after	♩	comes	▬
after	♩	comes	▬
after	♪	comes	│
after	♭♩	comes	○

130 A = 9
B = 2
The first row across totals 15; the second row 16; the fifth row 19 and the bottom row 20. Thus, the total increases by one in each successive row.

131 SPINNAKER

132 6,561
There are two sequences arranged alternately. In each sequence the number is the square of the previous number in that sequence. 6,561 is the square of 81.

133 A ¹/₂ revolution
B 2¹/₂ revolutions.

134 11
$(6 \times 11) - 24 = 90$

135 2.50

136

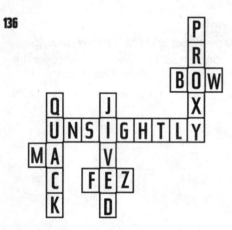

137 A 7; B C

	Black ball	White ball
1st move	D	A
2nd move	E	F
3rd move	F	D
4th move	G	B
5th move	A	G
6th move	B	E
7th move	C	C

138 5

Columns headed by an odd number add up to 30. Columns headed by an even number add up to 40. The last column adds up to 35, to which must be added 5 to bring it up to 40, as this column is headed by an even number.

139 x is 11; y is 61

In the first circle the number in the top left quarter is squared and then reduced by 1 in the opposite diagonal quarter; the number in the top right quarter is cubed and then 1 added to give the number in the opposite lower quarter.

In the second circle the same procedure is followed except that 2 is deducted from the squared number and 2 is added to the cubed number.

Therefore, in the third circle 3 is deducted from the square of 8 (64 becomes 61 – the value for Y), while 3 is added to the cube of 2 (8 becomes 11 – the value for X).

140 x is 9 or 24; y also is 9 or 24

In each case the numbers at the top are divided by 4 in the opposite quarter and 1 is added.

An alternative solution is that the numbers in the lower quarters are miltiplied by 4 in their opposite quarters and 4 is deducted from the result.

141 Horse No. 6   5-1 Against

		Amount to be staked to recover 100 including stake	
2-1	1	£ 33.3	
3-1	2	25	
4-1	3	20	
5-1	4	16.6	
6-1	5	14.3	
	6	?	
		109.3	
5-1	6	16.6	Add horse No. 6
		125.9	

Whichever horse wins he gains 125.9% as long as he has balanced his books.
(He receives £125.90 and pays out £100.00. His profit is, therefore, £25.90.)

142 9

The totals in the bottom quarters are half those in the opposite top quarters.

143 40

Add half the number on the left to its square root and arrive at the number on the right. Alternatively, the left hand column from top to bottom follows the progression of adding 5, 7, 9, 11, 13 and 15, while the right hand column adds $3^1/_2$, $4^1/_2$, $6^1/_2$, $7^1/_2$ and finally $8^1/_2$, bringing the last number to 40.

144 ABANDON

The two cards at the top represent the letters of the alphabet, as there are 13 in each suit. Thus hearts represent A to M, and diamonds N to Z. Therefore:

Ace of hearts	A
2 of hearts	B
Ace of hearts	A
Ace of diamonds	N
4 of hearts	D
2 of diamonds	O
Ace of diamonds	N

145 Ten minutes past eleven

The hour hand advances first 1 hour, then 2, then 3 then 4 (11 in X) and finally 5. At the same time, the minute hand goes back first 5 minutes, then 10, followed by 15, 20 (to 10 minutes past), and finally 25.

146 $18 \div 2 \times 9 + 24 - 5 = 100$

147 C

In A two letters are missed out.
In B three letters are missed out.
In C four letters are missed out with the exception of V, which should be U.
The numbers in D, E and F follow the same pattern.

148 33

149 Take reciprocal, i.e. divide into 1

4 hrs	=	1/4	= .25
5 hrs	=	1/5	= .20
6 hrs	=	1/6	= .166
8 hrs	=	1/8	= .125
			.741

Take reciprocal again $\dfrac{1}{.741}$ = 1 hr 21 mins

150 200m would only take 199 cuts not 200.
199 x 4 sec = 13.27 mins

151 D
As the black blocks are farther from the fulcrum the see-saw should go down on the right.

152 6/2 or: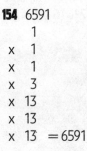

Apart from this domino, which equals 8, all combinations of numbers from 1-10 are accounted for:
1/0
2/0 and 1/1
3/0 and 2/1
4/0, 3/1 and 2/2
5/0, 4/1 and 3/2
6/0, 5/1, 4/2 and 3/3
6/1, 5/2 and 4/3
5/3 and 4/4
6/3 and 5/4
6/4 and 5/5

153 A
The area of the circle (based on the formula: multiply the square of the radius by 3.14 approx) is 3.97 square inches.
A is 4 square inches (the nearest)
B is 4.41 square inches
C is 3.80 square inches
D is 3.78 square inches

154 6591
         1
     x   1
     x   1
     x   3
     x 13
     x 13
     x 13 = 6591

155 AE, BH, CF, DG

156 K
Each row follows the same pattern of shading as in the first row, except for K, which should appear as in C, G and O.

157 B and C
They fit together like this.

158 14
The results are as follows:
1st throw 6 8
2nd throw 4 14
3rd throw 3 10
4th throw 1 8
5th throw 2 12
6th throw 6 20
7th throw 5 14

159 216225
Square the number on the left outside the brackets and place the result on the right inside the brackets, then cube the number on the right outside the brackets and place the result on the left inside the brackets. Repeat this procedure throughout, so the last line is 225 (15 squared) and 216 (6 cubed).

160 C

161 201 (add digits to previous number)

162 947 x 947 apples

163 E
B is the same as F
D is the same as C
A is the same as G

164 125
96 passes out of 125 give an average of 76.8%

165 C
In C there are 2 right-angled triangles. In the other rows there are 3 right-angled triangles and 2 isoceles triangles.

166 Here are nine possible combinations:
6   19 25;
8   17 25;
10 19 21;
4   21 25;
2   6 17 25;
2   4 19 25;
2   10 17 21;
4   10 17 19;
4   8 17 21.

167 1854
According to this mathematical formulai: $7!\left(\frac{1}{2}!-\frac{1}{3}!+\frac{1}{4}!-\frac{1}{5}!+\frac{1}{6}!-\frac{1}{7}\right)=1854$

168
```
      2 7 3 0
    2 9 7 0 4
  2 4 9 9 1 8
  2 7 8 3 0 4
      2 1 0 4
+ 2 7 9 9 1 8
  8 4 2 6 7 8
```

169 A
The figures in the quarters are transposed as in the top example and their shading or patterns are transposed in the same way.

170 27

In the top line the first number, 9 is divisible by 3; 8 is divisible by 4; 10 is divisible by 5; 18 is divisible by 6; 21 is divisible by 7; 16 is divisible by 8. hence the next number must be divisible by 9, and the only number that complies with this is 27.

171 X is 15; Y is 11

In the outer ring, going clockwise from 7, each number doubles the previous number and subtracts 1. hence x (coming before 29) must be 15. In the inner ring, each number doubles the previous number and adds 1. Hence y is 11 (double 5 plus 1).

172 C

The spiral turns the opposite way from the others.

173 99

After the first two terms each subsequent term is the sum of the two previous terms.

174 D

All the others contain one acute angle, one obtuse angle and one right angle. D contains two acute angles and on obtuse angle.

175 25

In the first row divide the numbers outside the brackets by 14 and put the results inside the brackets. Continue in th esame way, but next dividing by 15 and then by 16. In the last row divide by 17.

176 A is 7, B is 1, C is 8

With a four-figure total, the calculation is obviously addition and not subtraction. In order to reconcile the units with the tens. B must be 1 (the units total 7), so that 7 added to 4 in the tens gives 11, confirming that B is 1 (also confirmed in the final total). To give 2 in the final total, C must be *, so that the hundreds came to 12.

177 $4^1/_2$ or 4.5

In each quarter halve each total of the rings up to and including the centre. Thus, in the bottom left quarter: 24 plus 12 = 36, 11 plus 7 = 18, 6 plus 3 = 9. Therefore x = $4^1/_2$ or 4.5.

178 4

The first term is followed by the last term; the second term is followed by the penultimate term, and the third term follows the same procedure. Thus the series becomes: 25 24 22 19 15 10 4(x) – ie, decreasing by one more each time: -1 -2 -3 -4 -5 -6(x)

179 Matilda 19   Philip   17

180 $\dfrac{5289 \times (49 + 63) \times 4.5}{60 \times 60}$

  =   739.2 ft

181 AIK, BGH, CLN, DEF, JMO

182 AD BF CE

183 2,150
51 is midway between 3 and 99; 43 is midway between 7 and 79; 51 x 43 = 2,193, less 43 (midway between 9 and 77) = 2,150

184 16
Each number in the bottom row is the sum of the number above it and the previous number.

185 Sapphire (2)
    Emerald (5)
    Diamond (10)

186 2519 apples

187 C
The others are all the same

188 190

189 Wind-surfers
(spindrift = spray)

190 A

191 C, D E

192 B
The angle is 60°.
The others are 90°, 45° or 30°.

193 F

The design round the top should consist entirely of diamond shapes, as in B and L. In F one of the diamonds has become a square.

194

```
    130760
    130760
    130760
    130760
    130760
+   194215
    848015
```

195 X is 4; Y is 6

Expressing each letter as a number according to its position in the alphabet, the table appears as below, with what were originally letters circled:

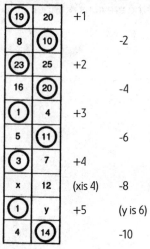

(19)	20	+1
8	(10)	-2
(23)	25	+2
16	(20)	-4
(1)	4	+3
5	(11)	-6
(3)	7	+4
x	12	(x is 4) -8
(1)	y	+5 (y is 6)
4	(14)	-10

196 BERLIN

The moves are as follows:

	Ball A	Ball B	Ball C
1st move	19	5	B
2nd move	7	12	E
3rd move	16	6	R
4th move	2	1	L
5th move	20	3	I
6th move	15	16	N

197 D and G
D (a house with an even number) should have a flat porch. G (a house with an odd number) should have a chimney stack.

198 3 – 1 – 1 – 4 – 8 – 8 – 8 – 8 – 3 – 4 – 3

199 Nylon hose

200 A
The smallest figure in the centre becomes the largest figure on the outside, while the other figures remain in the same order.

201 2
Spaced correctly the series becomes:
4 9 13 22 35 57 9 (2)
After the first two numbers, each subsequent number is the total of the previous two. The sum of 35 and 57 is 92.

202 B

203 114
The two numbers on the left inside the brackets are the sum of the digits on the left of the brackets. The number on the right inside the brackets is the difference between the sums of the digit on either side of the brackets.

204 9
There are two separate series here. starting with the first term and taking alternate terms thereafter:
6561 81 9 3. Each number is the square root of the previous number.
Starting with the second term:
256 16 4
Again, each number is the square root of the previous number.

205 E
The wards (the projections at the end) which turn the lock are different from those in the other keys.

206 A 8; B 5; C 7; D 1; E 9; F 3; G 6; H 2; I 4

207 C
The thread turns the opposite way from the others.

208 D
The figure is rotating clockwise.

209 The 9th spin

1st spin	19
2nd spin	3
3rd spin	9
4th spin	18
5th spin	32
6th spin	17
7th spin	27
8th spin	3
9th spin	ZERO

210 AE; BG; CF; DH

211 18
Each modern number in any one segment has a number in Roman numerals in its opposite segment. Starting with MDC (1600), this is doubled in the opposite segment to give 3200. Moving clockwise, IV is halved, to give 2 in the opposite segment. This doubling and halving continues, so by the time we get to IX (9), this must be doubled in the opposite segment to give 18, expressed in modern digits.

212 B
Examination of the top cubes reveals that they atre rotating forwards (confirmed by the changed positions of the two spots on the side). As far as the facing side is concerned, B C, D or E could be correct, but only in B have the two spots changed their positions in keeping with the forward rotation.

213 71
Each number is increased by adding the total of its digits to the number itself. So, 11 (1 + 1 = 2) becomes 13, 13 (1 + 3 = 4) becomes 17, etc.
Following this procedure, 58 (5 + 8 = 13) becomes 71.

214 2

215 38 (5 x 4) + (10 + 8)

216 B

217 D
A is the same as B; C is the same as G; E is the same as F

218 50746

(1 x 9) - 1	= 8
(8 x 9) - 2	= 70
(70 x 9) - 3	= 627
(627 x 9) - 4	= 5639
(5639 x 9) - 5	= 50746

219 E
B is the same as D; A is the same as C

220 Colony of Frogs
Horde of Gnats
Den of Snakes
Clutter of Spiders
Nest of Machine Guns
Park of Artillery
Doylt of Swine
Gang of Elks
Business of Ferrets
Volery of Birds
Hover of Crows
Drift of Wild Pigs

221 40mph

222 12
Opposite faces of the dice add up to 7. Therefore, moving horizontally from left to right and starting in the top row, opposite faces are: 3 1 6 2.

223 B
All the rows, horizontally and vertically add as follows:

Square 1	19
Square 2	18
Square 3	17
Square 4	16

In square B all the rows, horizontally and vertically, add to 15.

Alternatively, the numbers in square 1 add to 76. Those in square 2 add to 72. Those in sqyuare 3 add to 68, and in square 4 they add to 64. Therefore (decreasing by 4 each time) square H (60) must follow square 4.

224

225 With 24 people in the room you would in the long run lose between 23 and 27 out of each 50 bets. (This ignores February 29th).

226 X = 5; Y = 4
From the top square:
2 numbers total 13
3 numbers total 15
4 numbers total 17
5 numbers total 19
In the bottom square:
X is in a row of five and must be 5 to bring the total (14) up to 19;
Y is in a row of four and must be 4 to bring the total (13) up to 17.

227 X is 2
The number in the inner circle is the difference between the product and the sum of the three numbers in the outer circle.

228 C
In the top row the total of the hours to which the hands point is 50 (12, 4, 13, 17 and 4); in the second row the total is 40 (17, 6, 11 and 6); in the third row the total is 30 (11, 13 and 6); in the fourth row the total is 20 (9 and 11). Hence, in the bottom clock the total must be 10, and C (4 and 6) is the only one that gives this.

229 3 minutes
Take reciprocals

$6 = 1/6 = .166$
$4 = 1/4 = \underline{.25}$
$+ \qquad .416$

$12 = 1/12 = \underline{.083}$
$- \qquad .333$

$\dfrac{1}{333} \qquad = 3 -$

230 99 legs
Each leg requires 10 chops

231 $1\,1/3$
$\dfrac{11}{12} \times \dfrac{48}{33}$

232 D

233 7
$(7 + 14 + 9 + 1) - (6 + 9 + 7 + 2)$

234 $52 \times 16 = 400$ feet

235 A 8
B 16
C 24

236 C
The first five patterns indicate that they are globes, rotating anti-clockwise.

237 B

238 A-K, B-P, C-M. D-J, E-O, F-L, G-I and H-N

239 35

The highest prime number is 17, and the lowest even number is 6. The remaining numbers add to 137.

240 D

241 9

242 210
The 10 highest numbers (19, 7,16, 8, 11, 14, 9, 12, 5 and 20) total 121
The 10 lowest numbers (1, 18, 4, 13, 6, 10, 15, 2, 17 and 3) total 89

243 The reason Frank replied so quickly is that he had spotted that the digits 7 - 4- 6 - 1 add up to 18, and when the sum of the digits are divisible by 9 exactly, then the number itself is also divisible by 9 exactly. Therefore, in whatever order you arrange these four digits, the number produced will divide exactly by 9.

However, on this occasion, Frank was not correct, because by screwing the 6 on upside down, it becomes a 9, and then none of the resultant four digit numbers will divide exactly by 9.

244 4/1 against.
The number of pictures on the card does not affect the odds. The only thing that does affect the odds are the number of winning pictures and the number of losing pictures.

245 L
The middle heart has been changed to a spade.

246 One after another.

247 So were the other half.

248 E
A is the same as G, B is the same as F; C is the same as D.

249 (i) Globe A; (ii) Globe G
The globes are rotating anti-clockwise.
In (i) there are two vertical rows of spots situated adjacent to each other. At X one of these rows (the centre one on the first globe) will be on the blind side and only one row will be visible.
In (ii) there are three vertical rows of spots on one side of the globe only. On the other side there are no spots. Therefore at Y there will be one row visible, while in the next position of the globe all three rows will be on the blind side.

250 22, 286

Alternate numbers starting at 7, advance by 4, 5 and 6. The alternate numbers starting at 91 are 13 times the previous number.

251 The figure rotates $1/4$ turn anti-clockwise. the difference in shading remains constant throughout. In F the small outer circle and the triangle have changed places.

252 B

253 x = 840

y = 168

z = 24

Values of the shapes as indicated are: square = 4, circle = 5, and triangle = 6. The value of the rectangle is not indicated, but is obviously 7. This is ascertained from the relationship between 4 (square) and 28, or 5 (circle) and 35. From this it can also be seen that the values of overlapping areas are obtained by multiplying the values of the individual shapes that make up those areas. Confirmation of this is given by 140, which is the product of 4, 5 and 7.

Therefore, X is the product of the circle, square, triangle and rectangle; Y is the product of the triangle, rectangle and square; Z is the product of the triangle and square.

254 5

255 H

The faces are made up of four straight lines, five curves, two dots and one circle. In H there are only three straight lines.

256 28, 42, 41, 53

Four sequences alternate between columns:

Columns A & C

2, 5, 8, 11, 14 etc

Columns B & A

2, 4, 6, 8, 10 etc

Columns C & D

1, 5, 9, 13 ,17 etc

Columns D & B

3, 6, 9, 12, 15 etc

257 E
Acute angles have symbols at the end of the lines, as shown in the first row. Obtuse angles and right angles have different symbols.
In the second row the colours of the symbols are reversed (black becoming white and white becoming black), and in the third row they are reversed again.
Therefore, in E the circle and square are the wrong colours.

258 A, B, C and D are made up of circles and squares.
In A there is a circle inside a square inside a circle;
In B there is a square inside a circle inside a square;
In C there is a circle inside a circle inside a square;
In D there is a square inside a square inside a circle.
The third row is made up of triangles and circles, conforming in the same way.
In A the centre figure (the circle) is black; in B the midddle figure (the circle) is black; in C the outer figure (the square) is black; in D none of the figures is black.
The third row must conform in the same way.

259 X = 3
Y = 4
Z = 9
The total of each line, horizontally, vertically and diagonally will then be 15.

260 184
Double the first number and add 1;
double the second number and add 2;
double the third number and add 3.
Continuing in this manner:
double the sixth number (89) and add 6.

261 15
The lower number is the sum of the number above it and its preceding number.

262 1,024
The first number is squared to give the second number, which is then halved to give the third number. This is turn is squared to give the next answer, and so on.

263 Number 2.
In the first row there is one horizontal line (in the 7),
one vertical line (in the 1), one diagonal line (in the 7) and one circle (in the 6).

In the second line there are two of each.
In the third line there are three of each.
In the fourth line there are four of each.
There ARE four circles (in 896), but only three vertical horizontal and diagonal lines. Number 2 is the only figure which supplies all three.

264 Put the letter T in each blank space. Now start at the bottom left hand square and read up the first column, then along the top and eventually spiralling into the centre to spell out the word prestidigitation. A very magic word presented very squarely indeed!

265 8
A vase with a broad black band round the centre has a row of circles round its neck; if there is a broad black band with a thin line below it round the centre, there is a row of rectangles round the neck; if there is a thin line near the bottom of the vase there is a row of diamonds near the neck.
When there is a broad black band round the centre with a thin line above it there should be a double line going round the neck, but in number 8 there is only a single line.

266 F
In the first row the balls are arranged as follows:
A: 1 black ball; B: 2 black balls; C: 3 black balls; D: 4 black balls.
In the second row the WHITE balls should follow the same arrangement, so that F should have two white balls instead of three.

267 3
The total of the numbers on each side of the large triangle should be the same as the total on the same side of the small triangle. The total of the numbers on the left-hand side of the small triangle is 17, made up of 8, 1, 1, 1 and 6. The numbers given on the side of the large triangle are 2, 1, 4, 1, 2 and 4, giving a total of 14. Therefore the remaining number must be 3, to bring the total up to 17.

268 X= 420
Opposite numbers are obtained by multiplying the smaller number by one less than itself. In the first circle: 3 multiplied by 2 gives 6 and 8 multiplied by 7 gives 56; in the second circle 9 multiplied by 8 gives 72 and 12 multiplied by 11 gives 132. In the third circle 14 multiplied by 13 gives 182 and 21 multiplied by 20 gives 420.

269 B
Each pattern consists of four straight lines, four curves and four dots, except B, which has five curves.

270 1A. There is a dot missing.

271

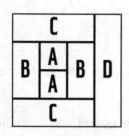

272 They are the numbers 2, 4, 6, 8 complete with mirror-image.

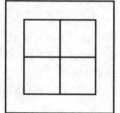

273 G

The handle is in the wrong position, as compared with B and D.

274 29

Opposite faces of a die add up to 7. Therefore, moving horizontally from left to right and starting in the top row, opposite faces are: 6 4 1 3 5 2 1 3 4

275 8

This is an ordinary 'doubling-up' series, but wrongly spaced. When correctly spaced, the answer becomes obvious: 1 2 4 8 16 32 64 128

276 A is 24; B is 7; C is 23; D is 7

There are four series. Starting with the first term and taking every fourth term thereafter:
3 4 5 6 7(d)
Starting with the second term and continuing in the same way:
27 26 25 24(a)
Starting with the third term:
1 3 5 7(b)
Starting with the fourth term:
32 29 26 23 (c)

277 C

278 1 in 24 or 23 to 1 (3 x 3 x 2 x 1)
The chances of spotting three balls correctly was exactly the same, as if three balls were spotted correctly, then four must be also.

279 A

280 55
In each quarter, add the numbers in the outer ring, then those in the next ring, and then the next.
In the top left quarter these totals descend:
40 39 38 37 (the single number in the centre).
In the top right quarter they descend:
23 22 21 20 (the single number in the centre)
In the right lower quarter they descend:
115 114 113 112 (the single number in the centre).
Therefore, in the lower left quarter they descend:
58 57 56 – and then, 55 (X).

281 FIR
The first letter is indicated by the position of the hour hand relative to the hours – in this case 6, that is sixth letter (F).
The next letter is shown by the position of the second hand. Here it is on the 9th second, and the ninth letter is I.
The third letter is indicated by the position of the minute hand. As it points to the 18th minute, it shows that the third letter is R – the 18th letter of the alphabet.

282 36

283 B

284 Express all ther tems as vulgar fractions:
$1^2/_3$ $2^3/_4$ $3^4/_5$ $4^5/_6$ $5^6/_7$ $6^7/_8$
Now it is obvious that the terms progress like this
123   234   345   456   567   678
and that the final term must be 789, expressed as a vulgar fraction as in the examples: 78/9.

285 15 miles
The man walks 10 miles at 4 mph = 2.5 hours
The dog runs 2.5 hours at 6mph and covers 15 miles

286 24 minutes

As I leave according to my usual schedule, it must be before 6.30pm when I pick up my wife. Because we have saved 12 minutes, that must be the time that it takes me to drive from the point I picked her up to the station, and back to that same point. Assuming it takes me an equal 6 minutes each way, I have, therefore, picked her up 6 minutes before I would normally do so, which means 6.24pm. So my wife must have walked from 6pm to 6.24 pm or for 24 minutes.

287 A Orange
B Red
C Indigo
D Cerise
E Magenta

288 D

289 61 (127) 71

The numbers on each side of the braackets alternately increase by 2, 3, 4, 5, 6, 7, 8 (and hence 9 and 10). To discover the number inside the brackets: double the number on the left and add 1, then 2 then 3, then 4, and finally 5 (122 + 5 = 127).

290 2' 8$^{1}/_{2}$"

291 Assume Horus is the greatest
"I am not" said Horus (LIE)
"Anubis is" said Isis (LIE)
"Isis is lying" said Anubis (TRUTH)

292 So that
1. No two consecutive numbers appear in any horizontal, vertical or diagonal line
from which it follows that:
2. No two consecutive numbers appear in adjacent (horizontal, vertical, diagonal) squares.

13	10	7	3
1	4	15	11
8	12	2	6
16	14	5	9

293 38 inches

294 E

295 B
The very small centre suit becomes the large outer suit. The next smallest inner suit becomes the next largest outer suit. The next smallest inner suit becomes the next largest outer suit. The largest outer suit becomes the smallest centre suit.

296 245 246   247
Each set of numbers starts by doubling the last number in the previous set and adding first 1, then 2, and so on. The last number in the penultimate set is 120, so the first number in the final set is 245 (240 + 5).

297 5116
Divide the number on the right outside the brackets by the number on the left outside the brackets to give the first number inside the brackets. The two digits on the right inside the brackets are the square of the right-hand digit of the number on the left outside the brackets. The remaining digit (the second inside the brackets) is the square of the digit on the left of the number on the left outside the brackets.

298 7
Male forenames are:
Leonard
William
David
Jim
Eric
Tom
(Alternate letters in the outer ring)

Female forenames are:
Iris
Mavis
Sarah
Vera
Ann
Amy
(Alternate letters in the inner ring)

299 29 cats each killed 73 rats.

300 271

1st throw (5) becomes	15
2nd throw (4) becomes	19
3rd throw (4) becomes	4
4th throw (2) becomes	28
5th throw (6) becomes	72
6th throw (3) becomes	93
7th throw (2) becomes	38
8th throw (2) becomes	2
	271

301 9

Divide the top number by the sum of the two facing numbers and the series becomes 2, 3, 4, 5 and 6 (if X is 9).

302 X is 22 and Y is 13

Fairly simple deduction, especially if you realized that there were no alternatives in the third horizontal row, which led to the solution for the first vertical row.

303 42

Each number represents its position in the square relative to the other numbers. So 21 has two blank squares above it and one blank square below it.

304 1901-1954. It is not possible to read 1955 boggle style.

305 A False
B True
C False

The near-side wheels rotate anti-clockwise, but the off-side wheels rotate clockwise! In C the acute angle is slightly more than 60 degrees, because by the time the minute hand reaches 10, the hour hand will have moved slightly past the figure 4.

306 J

The upper branches should point downwards, as in D, E and N.

307 315

3	**4**
2	**(15)**

The number in the centre squares is the product minus the sum of the three numbers in the corner squares around it. For example, in the top left hand quarter:
The product of 2, 3 and 4 is 24 and the sum of 2, 3 and 4 is 9: 24 - 9 = 15 – as shown in the adjacent corner square.

308 CHILDREN
Present time indicated – CH, A. Forward to 5.15 – IL, B. Back to 12.50 – DR, C. Back to 11.20 – EN.

309 A scores 78
B scores 80
C scores 84

310 + + + ÷ +, + + + + + ÷

311 JONQUIL
The moves result as follows:

	Ball A	Ball B	Ball C
1st move	G	8	J
2nd move	H	9	O
3rd move	A	4	N
4th move	E	6	Q
5th move	U	7	U
6th move	K	6	I
7th move	I	8	L

312 A, B J and K

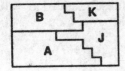

313 8 minutes

$$\frac{1}{9} + \frac{1}{24} - \frac{1}{36} = 0.12 \qquad \frac{1}{0.12} = 8 \text{ approx}$$

314 52642163

The numbers change from the number above in the following sequence:

ABCDEFGH   to   FDGBHEAC

315 10

316 C

Beginning with the segment containing 0 at approximately 10 o'clock in number 1, move clockwise. The segment next to it is removed in number 2 and in each subsequent figure. The number of segments in the circles decreases by one each time, so that from the initial 12 segments, the final circle contains only 6 segments.

317 Because only plus and minus signs are used there are many possible arrangements of these numbers.
Four examples are:
3+8-7+6-5+9-4
8-6-7+5+9+4-3
4-3+9+8+5-7-6
9-5+6-7+8+3-4

Any permutation of the numbers shown above (with the appropriate signs) would have satisfied the question. Of course, if division or multiplication had been required, the number of possible answers would have been very limited.

318 N

In no other figure is there a square within a square.

319 2

The total of the numbers in the triangle (3 sides), 51, is divisible by 3; in the square (4 sides), 44 is divisible by 4; in the pentagon (5 sides), 125 is divisible by 5. Therefore, in the hexagon (6 sides), the total of the numbers must be divisible by 6. As the present numbers total 70, 2 must be added to make 72. Of the numbers offered, only 2 will bring the total to a number divisible by 6.

320 B
The minute hand moves to where the hour hand was in the previous clock; the hour hand advances first one hour, then two hours, then three, and so on. After number 5 the hour hand must advance 5 hours (to 7).

321 3
Subtract the total of the numbers in the inner ring from the total of the numbers in the outer ring. In the third circle the outer ring totals 24 and the inner ring 21.

322 441
The lowest number is 3 and the highest number is 39, so the midway number is 21. The number nearset to the lowest number is 4 and the number nearest to the highest number is 38, so the midway number is 21 again. 21 multiplied by 21 is 441.

323 24

When viewed from above, there are 15 cubes; a further 9 can be seen when they are viewed from underneath. These nine can be seen more clearly if you focus your attention on the cubes with white bases and black side faces emphasizes here.

324 A
In A there are two right-angled triangles, one isosceles triangle and one scalene triangle. In all the others there are: one right-angled triangle, one equilateral triangle, one isosceles triangle and one scalene triangle.

325 4 1
  1 2

Start at the bottom left-hand corner and work up the first column, then along the top and round the perimeter, gradually spiralling into the centre and repeating the numbers 143682.

326 X is 10 and Y is 9

Consider the same segments that are occupied by x and y in the other circles:

8	9	10(X)	11
11	10	9(Y)	8

327 F

The black sides of the centre square rotate anti-clockwise; the black sides of the outer square rotate clockwise. In F the black sides of the centre square have rotated clockwise.

328 B and R

329 X is 12, Y is 0 and Z is 3

330 D

The black square moves anti clockwise, first one position, then two, then three, and so on. All the other squares move in the same way.

331 6

There are two separate series here. Starting with the first term and taking alternate terms thereafter:

625   25   5

Each term is the square root of the previous term.

Starting with the second term:

1296   36   6

Again, each term is the square root of the previous number.

332 MOSCOW

This problem is based on the fact that 26 cards make half of a full deck of playing cards, and there are also 26 letters of the alphabet. These 26 letters are represented by the cards at the top:

Clubs	Ace to 6	A to F
Spades	Ace to 6	G to L
Hearts	Ace to 6	M to R
Diamonds	Ace to 6	S to Z

Thus the cards at the bottom are:

Ace of hearts	13th letter	M
3 of hearts	15th letter	O
Ace of diamonds	19th letter	S
3 of clubs	3rd letter	C
3 of hearts	15th letter	O
5 of diamonds	23rd letter	W

333 Immediately to the left of the number 2

Start at the top right-hand corner and work along the top and back along the next row, counting 9 then 8 then 7 etc before entering each subsequent number.

334 $2^1/_8$ (approx 2.125)
Convert all the fractions into vulgar fractions:

$^1/_5$	$^2/_5$	$^3/_5$	$^4/_5$	$^5/_5$
$^1/_3$	$^3/_3$	$^5/_3$	$^7/_3$	$^9/_3$
$^1/_4$	$^4/_4$	$^7/_4$	$^{10}/_4$	$^{13}/_4$
$^1/_8$	$^5/_8$	$^9/_8$	$^{13}/_8$	$(1^7/_8)$

The final fraction could be $1^7/_8$ or $2^1/_8$
But as in the examples, vulgar fractions alternate with decimal fractions throughout. Also, as in the examples, the answer must be expressed in a unit and a fraction: $2^1/_8$
You may have converted all the fractions into decimal fractions. In all but the second row this would have been valid, giving a final answer of 2.125. There are, however, two fallacies:
a) there are no perfect decimal fractions for $^1/_3$ or $1^2/_3$, as they are recurring decimals, as in 2.33 recurring;
b) the already established alternating sequence of vulgar and decimal fractions should be maintained.

335 9
The numbers move one position clockwise at a time. Starting with 3 in the first square, the progression is:

3	4	5	6

Starting with 6 in the first square:

6	7	8	(9)

Starting with 5 in the first square:

5	6	7	8

Starting with 4 in the first square:

4	5	6	7

336 55
Divide the number on the left by 5 and multiply the number on the right by 5, entering the two results inside the brackets:

25	(55)	1

337 D

Sections only appear black in the final circle when they are white in both the previous circles looking across and down.

338

$$\frac{7}{11} \times \frac{33}{28} = \frac{3}{4}$$

339 5

Each smaller segments in A, B C add up to 20.

340 A

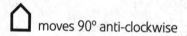

○ moves 90° clockwise   ⌂ moves 90° anti-clockwise

341

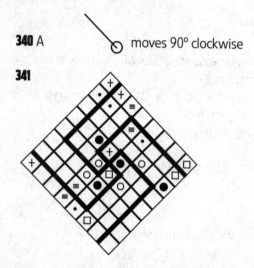

342 20 to 1 against.

343 A 130
B 25
C 122

A	9	15	21	25	27	33				
B	4	10	16	18	22	28	32	36	40	44
C	3	7	11	13	17	19	23	29		

344

So that when viewed in a mirror the numbers 1,2,3,4,5 appear in sequence.

345 26
A contains 4;
B contains 6;
C contains 6;
D contains 10

346 F
The top shape moves to the bottom in each following column.
F should be:

347

A	16	17
B	17	17
C	16	17

348 9 moves

A	7	6	5	4	3	2	1	9	8
B	1	3	5	7	9	2	4	6	8
C	2	5	8	2	5	8	2	5	8

349 3121

350 B and G

351 10

181	901
253	370
541	442
613	802
712	091

352 F   In all the others the middle three digits add to 10.

353 A=233, B=230 and C=69

The clues lie in the black sections, which indicate that, in the case of A, each number is the sum of the previous two numbers; in the case of B, each number is the sum of the previous three numbers; in the case of C, each number is the sum of the previous four numbers.

354 27

There are 9 balls in the bucket and 18 balls in the box.

355 5

Alternate numbers in A add to 30; alternate numbers in B add to 40; alternate numbers in C add to 14. 70 divided by 14 is 5.

356 72

357

358 A

Pinion A has 12 teeth, so 36 teeth will rotate in three revolutions. Pinion B will rotate clockwise. Although there are intermediate pinions between A and B, which may have led you to believe they would rotate in the same direction, the inner teeth on the very large annular ring will cause pinion B to rotate in the opposite direction to A.

359 2 ²/₃ pints
Each container will then hold 5 ¹/₃ pints - that is : ¹/₃ pint to B and 2 ¹/₃ pints to C.

360 K
A-H-N, B-I-P, C-M-O, D-L-F and E-G-J.

361 X is 2, Y is 1, Z is 3   All rows should add to 20.

362 C

363 31121314
Each number describes the number above, starting with the smallest digits.
So, 114213 has 3 x 1, 1 x 2, 1 x 3, 1 x 4

364 357
They are times without the dots with 15 minutes added each time, 2:57, 3:12, 3:27, 3:42, 3:57

365 30
Correctly spaced, the series becomes, 31, 28, 31, 30, 31, 30, 31, 31, 30, 31, 30(X) and 31 - that is, the number of days in the months of the year.

366 8
The corresponding sectors in all 3 circles add to 10. Starting at 1 in the first circle, the corresponding numbers thereafter are 1 and 8 (X).

367 783
The lowest number is 5; the nearest to the highest number is 49; the midway number between them is 27. The highest number is 51; the nearest to the lowest number is 7; the midway number between them is 29. 27 multiplied by 29 is 783.

368 I

369 A, B, E, G and J

370 A. 27 and 3 kilograms on one side; 1 kilogram on the other side. B. 27 and 1 kilogram on one side; 3 kilograms on the other side. C. 27, 3 and 1 kilogram on either side.

371 2 4 6 6 3 1 5   The digits are transposed in the same order throughout, but in each case the second digit on the left outside the brackets is omitted.

372 110   A=40 rpm, B=60 rpm and C=120. A, B and C together revolve at 220rpm; therefore D revolves at 110 rpm.

373 2B (dot missing)

374 DOGS   ANIMALS   REPTILES
LURCHER   BONGO   CAIMAN
CLUMBER   TUMBLER   SAURIAN
POINTER   AGUTI   TAIPAN
TERRIER   ROEBUCK   PUDDOCK

375 B. The diamond occurs once vertically and once horizontally. The dot occurs on the right and in the centre.

376 84
The numbers can be read diagonally on the face of a calculator working left to right.

7	8	9
4	5	6
1	2	3
0		

377 Youngest son 3.5 + 0.5 = 4
Second eldest son 1.5 + 0.5 = 2
Eldest son 0.5 + 0.5 = 1

378 4
Start with the arrow above X. In the opposite segment it is turned 90 degrees anti-clockwise. The next is turned 90 degrees clockwise. This alternating rotation is continued. Therefore, in the opposite segment to X the arrow must be turned 90 degrees clockwise (No 4).

379 A 5; B 1
There are 20 teeth on A and 30 on B. The large annular ring will rotate in the same direction as the driving pinion.
(A) After 4 revolutions of A the outer ring will rotate anti-clockwise through 80 teeth, causing the idling pinion to rotate through 2 revolutions (60 teeth) and an additional 20 teeth. (B) The driving pinion will rotate through 30 teeth - the same number as on the idling pinion, which will bring the black tooth on B to where it was originally (1).

380 20

Even numbers have prime numbers beneath them. Prime numbers have even numbers beneath them. 17 is a prime number, and must have an even number beneath it. The only even number in the third line is 20.

381 A. There are three separate series. Starting with the first letter and taking every third letter thereafter – ITALY: Starting with the second letter and taking every third letter thereafter – SPAIN: from the third letter – INDIA.

382 D

When adjusted, the clocks show the following times:
A from 3.27 to 12.57   B from 11.13 to 12.13   C from 1.44 to 12.24   D from 10.32 to 11.52
E from 5.21 to 12.19

383 B

Removing blocks X and Y leaves the following: diagram Turned upside-down, this corresponds with B.

384 2 4 12

The first number equals the number of CENTRE spots.
The second number is the total of the spots that surround the centre spots.
The third number is the total of the remaining spots.

385 0

There are three separate series, though digits representing tens are not placed adjacent to the units. For example, 12 is shown as 1 2. Starting with the first term, each third term thereafter multiplies the previous term by 3:
2 - - 6 - - - - 18 - - - - -
Starting with the second term, each third term thereafter multiplies the previous term by 4:
- 3 - -12 - - - - 48 - - -
Starting with the third term, each third term thereafter multiplies the previous term by 5:
- - 4 - - - 20 - - - - 100.
The final term (to complete 100) is 0.

386 D

(A) would show £200 interest;
(B) would show £182 interest;
(C) would show £189 interest;
(D) would show £210 interest.

387 3

The numbers represent the numbers of letters in each word of the question.

388 The numbers indicated by the short hand followed by the long hand are successive square numbers : 16, 25, 36, 49, 64

389 3.

(A) TRUE

(B) FALSE

(C) FALSE

(D) TRUE

390 1

The middle number is the difference between the sums of the three numbers on the left and the three numbers on the right.

391 30

In the second circle the number in the segment opposite the corresponding segment in the first circle is doubled. The number opposite X in the first circle is 15, so X is 30.

392 0

Correctly spaced, the series is:

1 2 6 24 120 720 5040

that is, multiplying by 2, 3, 4, 5, 6 and finally 7.

393 6 days

	hour hand	minute hand
1st day	6	5
2nd day	7	4
3rd day	8	3
4th day	9	2
5th day	10	1
6th day	11	12

394 14 and 15
14 is wrong because 5 has been placed beside 4; 15 is wrong because that domino has already been used (No. 14).

395 Three chances in four.
The possible combinations are
      black - black
      white - white
      black - white
      white - black
There is only one of these combinations where black does not occur, therefore, the chances of drawing at least one black ball are three chances in four.

396 X is 35
Y is 28
Z is 50
The number on the left in the top line is doubled to give the number on the right in the bottom line; the next number on the top line is multiplied by 3 to give its corresponding position in the bottom line; the next is multiplied by 4, and the next (7) is multiplied by 5 to give 25 (X) in the corresponding position in the bottom line.
The same procedure is followed in the second line from the top to establish the numbers in the second line from the bottom, so that 7 in the second line from the top becomes 28 (Y) in the second line from the bottom.
The number in the middle line is the sum of the other four numbers in the vertical column, so Z is the sum of 3, 7, 12 and 28 (Y), that is - 50.

397 (1) 195 miles; (2) 95 miles; (3) 20 miles.

398 C
   ■   moves 2 places anti-clockwise
   □   moves 2 places clockwise
   ●   moves 1 place clockwise
   ○   moves 3 places anti-clockwise
   ▲   moves 3 places clockwise
   △   moves 4 places either way

399 30
The number in the third vertical column is the difference between that in the right-hand column and the sum of the squares of the two left-hand columns.

Answers 400–410

400 1st over   1 3 4 5 6 7
2nd over   2 9 10 11   NOT OUT 8

401 B
One of the figures drops down on top of the other and the figures become transparent.

402 B
  A takes 2 hours, 45 minutes
  B takes 2 hours, 34 minutes
  C takes 2 hours, 40 minutes

403

ANIMALS	FISH	BIRDS
DASYPUS	LAMPREY	BITTERN
BANTING	MERLING	DOTTEREL
HAMSTER	SQUID	CHAFFINCH
BUBALIS	GROUPER	DOVE

404 81
$(121 = 11^2) - (100 = 10^2) - (81 = 9^2) - (64 = 8^2) - (49 = 7^2)$

405 10.35
3.20 - 5.45 - 8.10 - 10.35
Add 2h 25m each time

406 2 hours, 15 minutes, 20 seconds .

407 13
Reverse each number from first to last or vice versa. X is the reverse of 31.

408 14 minutes

409 C
Substitute numbers for letters according to their alphabetic position. Thus, the first relationship is between 6 3 7 4 and 7 6 4 3. The figures at the bottom are transposed in the same order.

410 E .